D1209217

AT a rough guess, we'd say that Ben Murphy's just about the cutest cowboy we've ever goggled at on the box . . . or anywhere else, for that matter! And you've got to admit he IS gorgeous! Even Glen, who's pretty cool about competition, doesn't mind staying in with his girl, when Ben's on telly!

Truth is though that, although he looks as if he could tame the Wild West single-handed, he lacks one thing that all cowboys have just *got* to have . . . and that's a love of horses! 'Course, he's a brave lad and definitely not one to admit when summat's got 'im worried, but even HE admits that there ARE moments when he'd rather be poundin' the beat on Softly Softly!

You see, it all started when the telly producers were casting the parts for Alias Smith'n'Jones. Ben's girlfriend at the time was not only terrific-looking (grrr!) but she was pretty smart with it! She'd suggested earlier that Ben should learn to do a bit of riding. It wouldn't do any harm . . . and it just could come in handy some day. (Believe it or not, some telly and film producers ask you to do the strangest things!)

Anyway, Ben went along with the idea, although he wasn't too happy about it and two weeks and ten lessons later, he was hurting in places that he hadn't even known existed! He was just about to call it a day, when he got a whiff of the part. He went along for the auditions and it didn't take people long to realise just how much he could brighten up the screens! Only thing was – could he ride? 'Course he could, he said – and got the part! Then came the first day on the set and Ben came face to face with his partner in crime. No, not Pete Duel – Midnight, a lovely BIG horse . . . with a film star's temper! Being a horse, of course, she wasn't quite as impressed with those lovely eyes and that gorgeous smile as *we* were.

Like we said, her name was Midnight but, by the end of the first week, Ben had got into the habit of calling her Pig! And no wonder! As you probably already know, it's hard enough staying on a horse when it's walking! But the Alias Smith And Jones series starts off with our boys being chased by a posse – and they had to do the take about a dozen times! By the end of the first day, Ben had to be helped out of the saddle! Not only that, but Midnight had a fancy for grass and she had the habit of chewing when she should have been moving!

Tough work, huh?! But Ben said he enjoyed it just the same and he'd even come to quite like Midnight, by the time the series was finished!

Ben Murphy Hates Horses!

ON THE OSMONDS

ALAN OSMOND

Date of birth: June 22nd., 1949.
Height: 6' 1".
Weight: 160 lbs.
Colour of eyes: brown.
Colour of hair: dark brown.
Hobbies: helping to produce records, writing songs . . . and snapping away with his new – very expensive! – camera.
Fave food: peanut butter sandwiches.
Fave drink: freshly-squeezed oranges.
Likes: sunshine and birdsong.
Dislikes: staying up too late and cold water – in any form!
Fave colours: red and yellow.
Other info: Alan plays lead guitar with the group . . . and he leads in lots of other ways, as well! Being the eldest in the family, Alan has to keep an eye on the other guys – just to make sure some clever fan doesn't pinch 'em!

WAYNE OSMOND

Date of birth: August 28th., 1951.
Height: exactly six feet.
Weight: 150 lbs.
Colour of eyes: brown.
Colour of hair: dark brown.
Hobbies: writing songs with his brothers and flying.
Fave food: breakfast fry-ups of ham 'n' eggs.
Fave drink: drinks milk by the pint.
Likes: having people around him, woolly jumpers, walking in woods just after rain – he loves the smell – watching television.
Dislikes: writing letters, having fittings for his stage suits, because he hates standing still for more than a minute at a time!

Fave colours: dark blue and white.
Other info: Wayne is very shy and quiet. In fact, last time he was in London, press people said that he told them nearly everything with his eyes – they're so expressive! He plays guitar and sax with the group, but he doesn't believe he's particularly talented. He says The Osmonds are successful because they like one another and work hard together.

MERRILL OSMOND

Date of birth: April 30th., 1953.
Height: 5' 11"
Weight: 150 lbs.
Colour of eyes: hazel and blue mixed!
Colour of hair: Light brown.
Hobbies: arranging music, writing songs, drawing everything in sight and playing the odd game of footy.
Fave food: Cornflakes, with lots of milk 'n' sugar.
Fave drink: Coke with loads of ice.
Likes: reading fans' letters, when he's down.
Dislikes: listening to old records the group have made.
Fave colours: all shades of brown.
Other info: Merrill is very friendly and enjoys meeting new people. He enjoys playing footy so much, The Osmonds have got together their own team.

JAY OSMOND

Date of birth: March 2nd., 1955.
Height: 5' 11".
Weight: 150 lbs.
Colour of eyes: brown.
Colour of hair: brown.
Hobbies: playing footy.
Fave food: cool, juicy melons.
Fave drink: lots of ice-cold water.
Likes: surprises.

Dislikes: always having to dodge fans, 'cos, he says, The Osmonds owe all their success to you.
Fave colours: black and red.
Other info: Jay is absolutely crazy about his drums and, when he hasn't got them near him, he'll beat out a rhythm on table-tops, bannisters and even walls!

DONNY OSMOND

Date of birth: December 9th., 1957.
Height: 5' 5".
Weight: 105 lbs.
Colour of eyes: dark brown.
Colour of hair: dark brown with chestnut streaks.
Hobbies: playing football.
Fave food: great chunks of cheese-'n'-bread, when he's hungry!
Fave drink: milk shakes, chocolate flavour, 'specially!
Likes: watching silent movies.
Dislikes: having to do schoolwork.
Fave colours: lilac and purple.
Other info: Donny's a home-lovin' boy and, although he likes travelling to foreign countries, he's always glad to get back to The Osmond homestead!

JIMMY OSMOND

Date of birth: April 16th., 1963.
Height: 4' 9" (and still growin'!)
Weight: 7 sts. 5 lbs. (and gettin' heavier!)
Colour of hair: straw blond.
Colour of eyes: greeny-blue.
Hobbies: swimming, football.
Likes: girls!!
Dislikes: being shorter than his other brothers.
Fave food: freshly-baked bread.
Fave drink: hot chocolate.
Fave colours: red and white checks.
Other info: He's already a superstar in Japan, would you believe!! and he's already been awarded several gold discs.

HERE IT IS...

THE SAD SECRET BEHIND DAVID CASSIDY'S SMILE

He's got everything a gorgeous guy could want . . . almost.

He has the sort of outright looks that superstars are made of; a pearly white smile, friendly twinkling brown eyes, shining chestnut hair that tumbles neatly onto his collar . . . just long enough for Mums and Dads to tut-tut, but not so long it looks untidy.

The face is always beautifully tanned, the features soft and relaxed, the body . . . rather nice!

No wonder that David Cassidy's picture smiles down from a million bedroom walls. He's a fine actor who managed to get good reviews in a Broadway show (New York) even 'though it closed after a couple of nights.

When the Partridge Family came along, he was hired as an actor. When it became an International success, the TV company bosses decided to release records using the Partridge Family name, but having session musicians and singers on the discs.

They were over the moon when they discovered David had a better than average singing voice to go with his good looks and acting talent. So no wonder that he's a very wealthy fella!

TV and best-selling records have boosted him to stardom, whereas the Partridge Family, he was just one of scores of struggling young actors trying for that big break. Suddenly he was hot property, in demand in half the countries in the world and it didn't take him long to realise that he can only be in one place at a time.

Nor did it take him long to realise that in this business it's dangerous to say 'no' to people!

So he's got everything a guy could want . . . except the thing that most fellas of his age treasure most, his freedom. But he's got the intelligence to know that this is all part of the job — the price that has to be paid.

And if the ever-present smile for the never-ending photo-graphers is sometimes there more by force of habit than natural joy, well that isn't his fault.

But there *is* another reason why David isn't as happy as he should be. Remember his parents were divorced — that left a big hurt that took a time to heal.

Then he got over it and on the set of the Partridge Family got to know his stepmother Shirley Jones very well. Sadly his father — actor Jack Cassidy — and Shirley broke up too, leaving David wondering about marriage.

Every superstar from the Beatles and George Best down-wards has been faced with the problem 'Does this girl want to know me for who I am or what I am?'

It's a question that seldom has an easy answer but David has the extra burden of two broken relationships always in the back of his mind.

Oh sure, there are girls a-plenty. That's the trouble. How does he pick a girl when there are thousands pressing forward to grab a lock of his hair? How does he politely ask a girl for a date, when every word is drowned in a roar of screams? No wonder that he hides away more and more.

It's difficult getting to the top in David's chosen profession. It's even more difficult staying there and life, when it seems it doesn't belong to you any more, must get almost unbearable.

No wonder we see the smile that helped David to stardom less and less these days.

THE TWINS ARE HUNG UP ON HAMBURGERS

Andy and David Williams are two gorgeous all-American guys! When they were over here, they told us they loved everything British — 'specially the girls! In fact, there was only one thing about home that they missed . . . and that was a big juicy hamburger!

INGREDIENTS (enough for six hamburgers)
1lb. of minced meat
1 egg
¼lb. Cheddar cheese, grated
Worcester sauce
salt and pepper to taste
1 onion
some sweet pickle
tomato sauce
mustard

Put the minced meat into a bowl and break it up with a fork. Add the grated cheese, and a drop of Worcester sauce. Break the egg in a cup, beat it up and add it to the meat. Sprinkle salt and pepper to taste. Cover the grill pan with silver foil (this stops the bits of mince from falling through the mesh!) Then, take a heaped tablespoonful of meat from the bowl and shape it with a spoon, till it's flat and round. Transfer it to the pan and repeat the process till all the meat has been used up. Put the pan under the grill with the heat turned on full. Cook the hamburgers for five minutes on each side. Meanwhile, chop up the onions finely. Then put the chopped up onion on a large plate and arrange around it a dollup of mustard, a dollup of sweet pickle and a dollup of tomato sauce! Serve up the hamburgers with chips.

SOUP FROM THE SWEET!

As lots of travelling popsters will tell you, eating when you're on the road is a luxury you can't always afford! Mick Tucker of The Sweet spends nearly all his time grabbing meals up'n'down the country and HE says there's nothing makes you feel better quicker than a good hot plate of soup!

This is a lickle recipe which Uti picked up when she was on holiday .

INGREDIENTS (enough for three)
1 pint of cold water
1 tablespoon olive oil
2 cloves of garlic
3 eggs
stale bread
salt and pepper

They sound pretty odd, we know, but they taste terrific when put together — like so! Put the cold water in a saucepan and add the olive oil. Bring to the boil. Meanwhile cut the cloves into tiny pieces, then, when the water is boiling, add the garlic and allow to simmer for a few minutes, till it gets soft. Add salt and pepper to taste, then, VERY CAREFULLY!! break the eggs into the water, one at a time.

Allow them to poach for two or three minutes, but don't allow the yolks to harden.

Break up the stale bread and cover the bottom of each soupplate with it. Then, lift out each egg with a spoon and lay it on top of the bread. Afterwards, pour the soup in.

DAVE RAVES ABOUT CHICKEN RISOTTO!

Dave Farmer of Blackfoot Sue eats enough for himself AND his brother Tom! Still, he's a gorgeous growin' lad and he needs his grub to give him all the energy he uses up playing with the band! He tells us he's got no favourite food . . . but he'd never say no to chicken! Here's a recipe he couldn't refuse!

INGREDIENTS (enough for three)
1 cup diced left-over chicken (from Mum's Sunday roast!)
1 cup rice (uncooked)
1 onion chopped finely
small tin tomatoes
small packet frozen peas
¼lb. chopped mushrooms
1 chicken stock cube
2½ cups hot water
some butter for frying

First, melt the butter in a saucepan. Then add the onions and fry gently for two minutes. Add mushrooms and fry for another two minutes. Add chopped chicken and tomatoes. Put cube in a bowl and pour over the boiling water. Add rice to saucepan and leave for a couple of minutes, till it turns golden, then pour the chicken stock into the pan. Add the frozen peas, salt and pepper, bring to the boil, then reduce heat and simmer for twenty minutes or until rice is cooked.

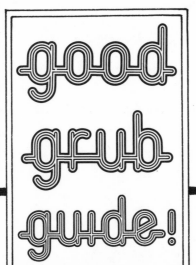

good grub guide!

SOMEONE, SOMEWHERE NEEDS A GIRL LIKE YOU WHO ??

THE QUESTION IS

S'true! There's a guy out there who's looking for a girl just like you – only he doesn't know it yet! It's obvious he's searching in all the wrong places, which is why he hasn't met you yet! But you never know, you could get together sometime soon . . . and it'll help things a whole lot if you recognise 'im! So do our quiz and then you'll be all set for your meeting with Mr. Right!

What kind of food do you enjoy eating most?
b) nothing in particular – usually snacky things which you always have lying around.
d) anything exotic – Chinese nosh f'r'instance.
c) lots of fresh things like fruit and vegetables.
a) mum's home cookin'!

What kind of clothes would you feel happiest and most attractive in?
d) the latest gear in shiny materials and velvet.
c) feminine dresses and high shoes.
a) scruffy ol' jeans an' T-shirts.
b) clothes that are casual, but unusual all the same.

What do you think is the most attractive thing about you, as far as boys are concerned?
a) the fact that you'll try anything once . . . and you usually enjoy it.
c) the fact that, when you're serious, you talk a lot of sense.
d) the fact that you can always look that little bit special, when you're going out.
b) the fact that you can keep pace with a boy's ever-changing moods.

Which gift would please you most?
c) an identity bracelet with HIS name on it.
d) a surprise night out to somewhere you've always wanted to go.
a) a bunch of freshly-picked Spring flowers.
b) a scarf, or something small to wear.

I am № B

What depresses you most?
a) being unsure.
b) being alone.
c) being misunderstood.
d) being ill.

**You and your guy have a tiff.
How do you feel afterwards?**
d) OK. You think the odd set-to brightens life up and keeps you on your toes.
a) Fine. You're the sort who argues all the time – in the friendliest way poss!
c) Better. It's important always to be honest and it helps to clear the air.
b) Shattered. You hate having arguments.

Now Check Your Score!
Well, the answers you've given to the questions, give us a good idea of the kind of girl you are . . . and the kind of guy who'd love you for it!!!

Mostly a's
No doubt about it – you're a girl and a half! You're everything that guys think girls ought to be – uncomplicated, natural, warm . . . and very feminine! You're definitely the marrying kind and you'd make home a nice place to come back to. You put your boy before everything – which is the way he likes it – and you're not too jealous for comfort. This also makes him feel good, cos he's used to being around lots of people and he can't be with you alone for twenty-four hours a day – much as he'd like to! The perfect match for you would be darlin' Donny – we're sure it'd be love at first sight if he clapped eyes on you! Still, if that's out of the question there are lots of luv'ly guys just like him, who'd appreciate you every bit as much!

Mostly b's
You're a very special kind of girl and you're meant for a very special kind of guy. You're never easy to please and, although lots of guys will ask you out on dates you'll turn most of 'em down. Which might mean that you're a little on your lonesome to begin with, but, when you meet Mr. Right, you'll agree that he was worth waiting for! You're sensitive, 'though not many people realise it and that often makes you unhappy. Never mind, the guy you'll team up with will feel just the same and he'll always know just what to do to please you – which can't be bad! Come to think of it, you're the perfect girl for David Cassidy – we've a good mind to give 'im your address! If you can't get David, look out for someone like him. And you'll find he's been looking out for you, too!

Mostly c's
Who's a shy one, then?! It takes a long time to get to know you but, once people get through to you, you're a luv'ly girl to have around! What's nice about you is the fact that you're reliable – a guy never has to worry about you disappearing the first time another good-lookin' fella comes along. Not only are you a great girl – you're a fabulous person, too and, as any Beautiful Couple will tell you, being a nice person goes a long way to having a terrific relationship. You're not bossy, but you're very sensible and you can help your guy make important decisions, without him realising you had anything to do with it. Marty Kristian's looking for a girl just like that – what a shame he hasn't met you yet! Still, someone like him would suit you just as well. So keep your eyes open!

Mostly d's
No doubt about it – you're a bundle of fun, from platform soles to the top of your razzle dazzle hairdo! You know that life's for living and you're not wasting one precious minute! Trouble is, you move so fast, not many guys can keep up with you! Although you're a very warm person, we'd rather have you as a friend than an enemy, 'cos you're pretty powerful stuff. What's more, you're the kind of girl who'll stand by your guy when things get rough and, since he's exactly like you, this'll happen all the time! You're decisive, sure of yourself and others expect you to take the lead. The guy you're looking for is just the same, but he's already discovered that it's tough at the top – 'specially when you're on your own – and he'd welcome a bit of company. The guy who'd most appreciate your many charms is Dave Hill of Slade. So, if you happen to have met his double, try getting to know him better!

"Er Micky, 'ow does that chord go again?"

THE THINGS POPSTERS SAY!!

You know how it is at a gig. When you're watching your fave popsters on stage, there's so much noise around that it's hard to hear what they're *playing,* never mind what they've got to say!

Anyway, we were looking through our files at some of the pics we've taken recently and, once we'd started imagining what they *could've* been yelling, we fell about laughing! Hope you enjoy 'em, too.

"Ooh honestly, I haven't a *thing* to wear!"

"It's all very well smilin', but the camera's over there!"

"I propose brothers, that we strike!"

"I've heard of togetherness, but this is ridiculous!"

"No, I couldn't tell it from butter!"

"If I go cross-eyed, it looks like we've got a full audience!"

"Alright, you just wait till I find out who pulled her 'ead off!!"

Bolan Is Beautiful!

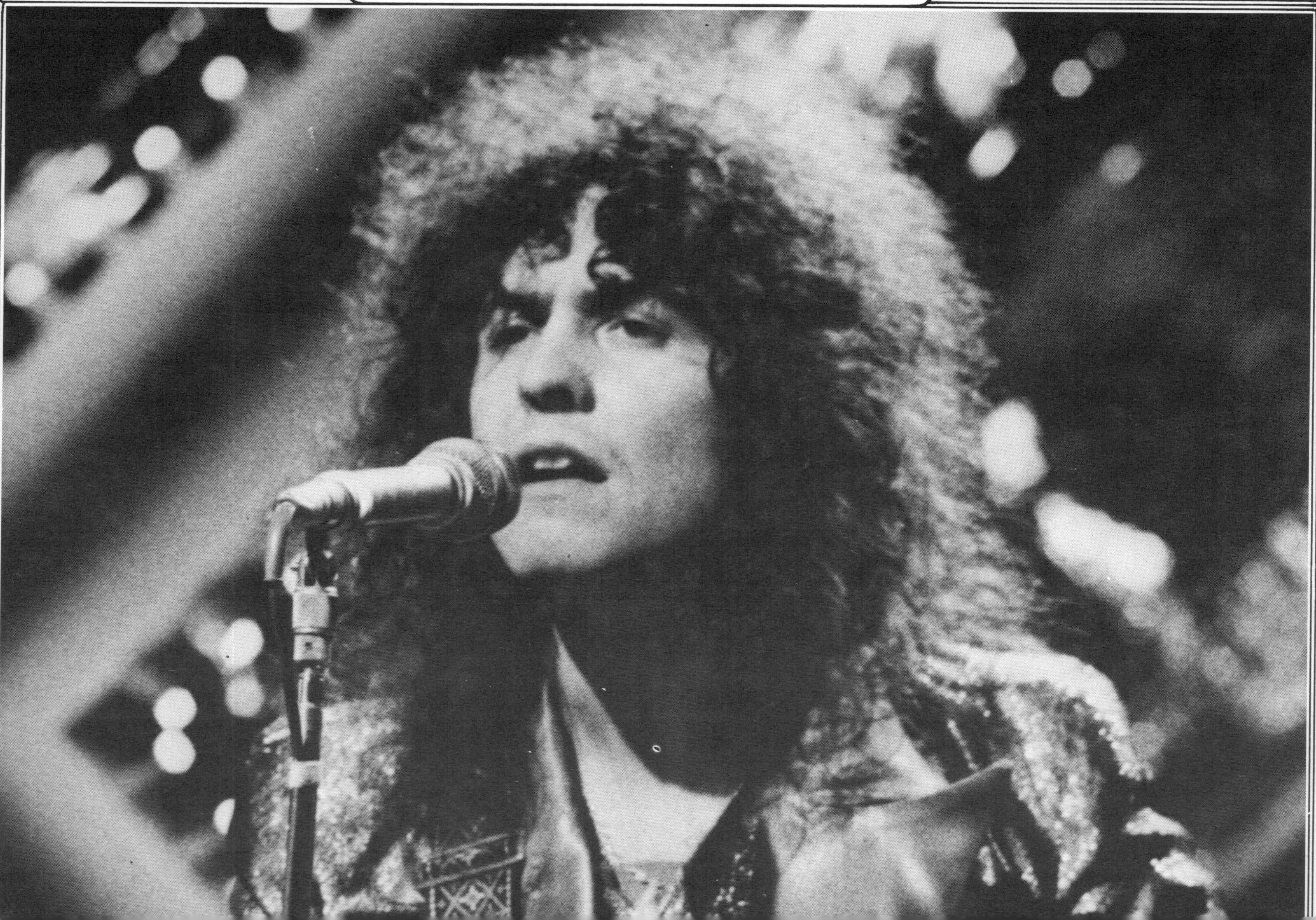

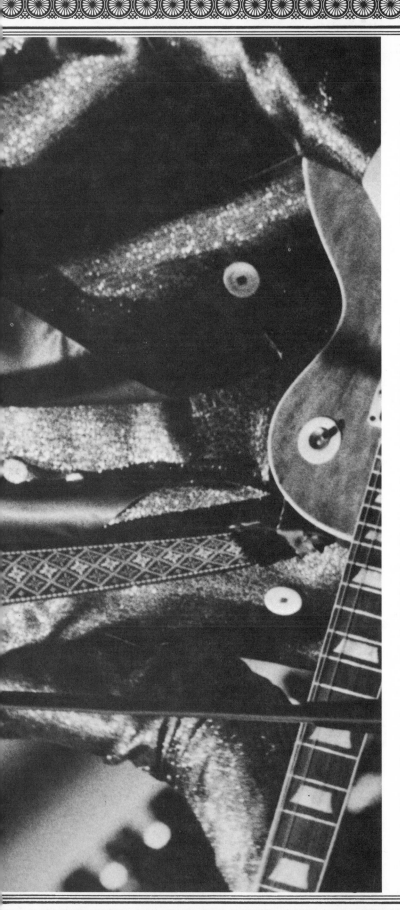

S'true! Marc Bolan is a beautiful person and you can be sure he's nearly always thinkin' beautiful thoughts! He always tends to see the best in people, overlooking their faults and, when you talk to him you get the feeling that, although he's listening very closely to everything you say, he understands a lot more just by looking at you! He has this mysterious gift of being able to look into and through

people and he's able to tell you lots of surprising things about yourself – even if he's only been with you for five minutes!

Of course, it's all in the stars! He can tell that a stranger is a Gemini or a Libran, or whatever, just by the way they walk, the clothes they wear and the little things they say. It's a handy gift to have, huh? And one that Marc wouldn't

change for the world!

Marc also loves beautiful things, as you can tell by some of the gorgeous shimmery clothes he wears and the way he takes such care of that thick, dark, curly hair of his! Even his name – which was originally Feld and which was changed by his record company into Bowland – was changed by Marc to Bolan, 'cos he thought it looked nicer that way!

And it goes without saying that Marc also loves beautiful words and music. He has written books of dreamy poetry, as well as mysterious Science Fiction novels and he always wants to discover more and more about music. One day, he thinks, he'll be ready to write some symphonies! All we know is, if the symphonies are as beautiful as Marc himself, we'll be more than ready to listen!

No matter how much care you take over your clothes and make-up, there are ten little things that can ruin the whole

FOR STARTERS!

Forget about fiddly nail massages. Instead, choose an all-in-one hand cream, then every time you rub it into your hands, just see that a little goes around the base of each nail and into the surface, too. Gradually, nail health will improve the painless way! buy Proteinail, or Innoxa All-In-One.

FILE FACES!

Did you know that running a metal file under nail-tips is just doing damage? It roughs up the underneath, making a surface that dirt sticks to more easily, and weakens the nail from the underneath, so it splits and flakes more easily. Use a soft orange stick, and if you HAVE to use that old metal nail file, protect the tip with a wisp of cotton wool or a fraction of a face tissue, first. A little ordinary hand cream on the cotton wool will help clean any nails which might have been scratched earlier.

NAIL NOSH!

Nails are made of the same basic material as hoof-and-horn, so any foods made from these basic animal proteins will help your nails grow stronger. That means gelatine, or jellies made from gelatine.

ROUGH STUFF!

Ridges on the nail surface are ugly but it's quite harmless to smooth them out VERY GENTLY with a light touch of the emery board, as long as you follow this up with a coating of one of the nail-strengthening fluids. These are like varnishes, but actually bond the nail surface and toughen it. Look for Cutex Strong Nail.

NAILED!

Nail shapes give away your character! Square nails are practical, pointed nails on the catty side, softly-rounded ovals very feminine and sexy! NEVER file 'em down at the sides, though, whatever the basic shape – it weakens the nail. Clipping is better – encourages growth, doesn't weaken. When you've clipped to the shape you like, finish with a light filing with an emery board.

SMOOTHLY!

Cracks between the bases of the fingers are rough to the touch, ugly to look at and a real health hazard, because this is how germs get in. Always dry thoroughly between your fingers and rub in cream afterwards. This applies to the sides of the nails, often ignored and splits and cracks here are painful.

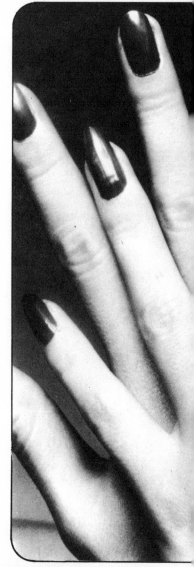

PHOTOGRAPH BY ELIZABETH ARDEN

UP!

ook . . . and every one of 'em
re nails!
o start getting them in
rim now, just in case
ou've got to show
our hand later!

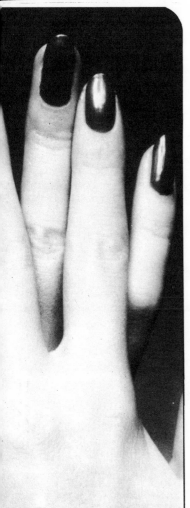

A BIT 'ER POLISH!

No varnish will stand up to a hammering if you don't allow it to get really hard before you expose it to life! Use fine coats, which dry quickly to a diamond-hard finish, and allow three coats for a varnishing, if you expect your manicure to last more than a couple of days. If you haven't the time, settle for a quick single coat, just to last the evening and remove it at the end of the day. Always brush varnish on in two strokes for the small nails, three for the large ones – from base of nail to nail tip. Don't overload the brush to begin with.

COLOUR CON!

Beware of varnishes that settle. Most good brands have now over-come this, and in the shop, however long the bottle has stood, the colour should look the same all the way down. If it has settled, it takes ages to shake it enough to mix it thoroughly and if you try to use it before you have mixed it properly, you will lose the pearlising and hardening ingredients, so the finished polish will be flat, and 'soft'.

KEEP 'EM CUTE!

Don't pick cuticles! Long ones will drag, and cause hang-nails, but they need never get into that state if you push the cuticles gently back after washing your hands, while the skin is still soft and pliable. If you *do* have cuticles that need more treatment than this simple remedy, use a cuticle-removing liquid, there is one in all good manicure ranges including Cutex, Max Factor, etc., which soften, clean and remove unsightly cuticle growth.

NAIL NIBBLERS!

If you REALLY want to cure nail-biting, you'll remember to use a brush-on colourless liquid such as Stop It, which nudges your memory, because every time fingers slip absent-mindedly into your mouth, the terrible taste reminds you! Even so, it takes two months to grow a decent nail if it's been nibbled practically to the bone. Meantime, shape them as they grow as far as you are able, as this will stimulate growth, and cover the most unsightly ones with plastic nails, for special dates at least.

TAKE 'EM OFF!

Varnish remover will not harm nails, provided it is a good brand, but all the same it is unwise to soak nails in it. Just use the minimum you need to, to take off old polish, and if your nails are slightly dry or brittle, brush a little olive oil in afterwards. If you intend to re-varnish right away, though, use a nail-strengthening fluid instead. If you want to thin down thickened varnish, you can use a little remover, but if nails are very delicate, it is better to use a special thinner, such as the Woltz Italiana one.

MEET THE PAUL FAMILY

It's pretty obvious to anyone who watches The New Seekers in action, that they actually enjoy working together. They do, too and they also happen to like each other very much – which is just as well, since they practically live in one another's pockets all year round! They're just like one big happy family . . . but then, they've had lots of previous experience!

Lyn Paul certainly knows what it's like to be part of a crowd – she grew up in one! As well as a luv'ly mum and dad, she has two brothers and three sisters. That's some of the Paul family in the pic and we can't decide who's the prettiest!

Cathy, on the left of the pic is eleven, Lyn's holding Nichola, who is five, the good-looking guy is Paul and he's seven and Mandy, on the right, is thirteen. Lyn's also got a brother of twenty-two. He couldn't make it to POPSWOP in time to be in the

pic, but we've seen him an' he's gorgeous! He helps to run their dad's haulage business in Manchester – that's where all the family used to live, until recently.

Trouble was, though, that Lyn's a real family girl at heart and, when it turned out that she'd have to spend more and more of her time in London, she got to thinking that, if she couldn't be with the rest of the family, then they'd just have to be with her! So, she bought this fabulous house just outside Reading and it really is like something out of a dream! It has lots of beautiful rooms, the girls have their own bedrooms designed just the way they want them . . . and there's even a stream running at the bottom of the garden, with swans swimming around in it! Lyn's family love it, and no wonder . . . but the girls *were* a bit sorry to leave Manchester, at

first. This was because they were all attending the Miss Lawrence Dancing School back home and they got a lot of fun out of it. Not only that, but their training helped them to get lots of parts on television, too.

Still if they've got anything like the talent that's made Lyn so well-known, coming to London could be the best thing they ever did!

During 1973, The New Seekers were travelling the world a lot on tours and they spent an awful lot of time in America in particular. Although it was pretty exciting and the group wouldn't have missed it for the world, it DID mean that they had to find flats to stay in while they were there. By the end of the tour, Lyn was dying to get back to her family and the house with the stream at the bottom of the garden. We think she's a very lucky girl. In fact, they're just one big lucky happy family!!

Donny Osmond

Slade

David Cassidy

Marty Kristian

Michael Jackson

Rod Stewart

New Seekers

Ben Murphy

ELTON? HE'S A STAR, MAN!

He's a rocket man. He soars to the stars and flies into orbit at the top of the charts. He wears silly clothes, writes lovely songs and is so rich at the ripe old age of twenty-six that, even if he never did another day's work in his life, he could live to the end of his days in splendid idle luxury.

But Elton John isn't built that way. He got where he is today with a struggle and a lot of hard work. He put up with a lot of criticism. He gave up his privacy. And through it all, Elton kept right on smiling.

Now he's a giant. His new albums are eagerly awaited by fans and critics alike. His concerts are sell-outs and he's a director of Rocket Records, a happening label for new talent.

We remember the first time we met Elton. We had a chat together and he was dead chuffed because he had just learned that Cilla Black and the American hit group Three Dog Night had recorded two of his songs. There was something about him then that made us think we were sitting next to a tomorrow superstar.

The next time we bumped into him was at a reception to celebrate a million sales of one of his albums.

What's his incredible success brought him? Firstly a gorgeous modern house which he's called Hercules on a beautiful private estate not a stereo blast from Windsor Castle.

It's a ranch-type bungalow standing in its own grounds complete with floodlit swimming pool. "The water is kept at about ninety-five degrees day and night," says Elton, "so that I can do a few lengths any time I want. It's great coming home from a hot sweaty day in London, going straight to the shed by the pool to change and diving straight in."

The inside of the house is a weird and wonderful assortment of odd bits and pieces; a huge wooden globe which is a present from his mum (who looks after Hercules while Elton is away touring) a stuffed boar from Berlin, a stuffed bear from New York and a magnificent lion which stands proudly – and very still we're glad to say! – on his bedroom carpet.

One of his proudest possessions is a toy koala bear, a gift from pianist Winifred Atwell – one of Elton's first idols.

"I'm a maniac for collecting stuffed toys. Maybe it's because they always stay the same – they never turn nasty."

Elton has developed an interest in gardening, which is just as well, 'cos the garden isn't exactly a window-box!

"I feel very guilty when I look out of the window and see the grass six inches long and weeds strangling the flower beds."

"I force myself into the mood, get on some old clothes and get out there with the mower or a pair of shears."

He has his eyes firmly fixed on some property next door which he'd like to buy to enlarge his grounds. Not more gardening?

"You must be joking," he exclaimed. "No, looking forward a couple of years, I'd like to have my own little entertainments centre right on my doorstep.

"I'd like to build a tennis court, a squash court which would never be out of use because I love squash, a small cinema and a studio. Now that I've actually taken the plunge and moved out of London I reckon on staying here for years."

Elton had the whole house re-decorated after he moved in. Just before the painters got busy, he gave a wild party. It was just as well the shindig was *before* the decorating, otherwise he might have needed another coat of paint!

"It was incredible! Two hundred and fifty people in my living room! Carpets were burned, walls were damaged and such a lot of stuff got broken but I wasn't too bothered about that."

"It was a sort of last fling before the house got its new look. Mind you, I'll think twice before giving a party like that again!"

Happiness is obviously the other thing that success had meant to Elton. Like everybody else he enjoys being liked but, for a performer and songwriter, it's even more important that they're admired and respected.

"I feel very contented now," he says. "The music is getting the recognition and I've achieved far more than I ever thought possible."

There *was* a time he was threatening to retire about now and spend his time lending a hand to talented musicians, singers and songwriters who weren't getting the breaks. Well, he's doing that via Rocket Records but we're glad to say the day when Elton hangs up his colourful costumes and puts the sheet over his piano looks as far away as ever!

25

Success was no overnight affair for Slade . . . even if their 'struggle' for fame and fortune *did* include a six weeks cabaret stint in the Bahamas! From their humble beginnings in Wolverhampton where they once worked for a few shillings a night, it took a lot of hard work, confidence, sweat and a few rumbling tums before they finally emerged as the happy stomping band of chart-busters they are today.

The strange thing is they've never really changed in the six years they've been on the road together, either as people or musicians.

As Noddy Holder puts it: "We've always done what comes naturally and even when things weren't looking too bright, we had enough confidence to think that one day the pop fans would come round to our way of thinking."

And come round we certainly did! These days Slade couldn't bring out a dud record if they wanted to. They can name their own price for concerts. But how long will it last? How will the group change? How will Noddy, Jimmy, Don and Dave change as people?

First the band.

"For a start," says Jimmy, "we're going to be around for a long while to come. The word 'solo' just doesn't exist for us.

"Sharing the bad times brings you a lot closer together and I can't see anyone wanting to quit until we all decide we've done as much as we possibly can as a group."

Do they figure to still be bopping and rocking their way from Teddington to Texas in five years time?

"Who knows?" replies Noddy. "We can only play the sort of music we feel at home with and right now I can't imagine us doing anything else but rock'n'-roll. But we can definitely get a lot better and I suppose it's possible that one day Slade might put out a romantic ballad . . . all slushy and violins."

"We'll still be bashing away at 30," laughed Dave Hill. "Slade will always be at their best on stage. I think the daftest thing the Beatles ever did was pack up gigging. Shutting yourself away in recording studios for months on end does you no good at all."

But what about the boys themselves? Doesn't the pace at which they live their lives get a bit frightening? Won't they be too tired or even too rich in five years time to keep it up? How do they see themselves in 1978?

"I suppose there's a chance we might act a bit more grown-up," suggested Don.

TAKE A LOOK AT SLADE'S FABULOUS FREAKED~OUT FUTURE !!

"No chance!" yelled Dave. "This business keeps you very very young at heart!"

"We'll never be big-time businessmen," said Noddy. "We're just not cut out for that behind-a-desk bit."

"We'll never be big-time *anything*," added Jimmy. "We've got as far as we have partly because we've kept our feet on the ground and been very careful about behaving like stars. We act big on stage which is where the fans want it, but anywhere else we're ordinary blokes from Wolverhampton who enjoy the company of the mates we've always had in the pubs we've always drunk in.

"Obviously there *will* be changes – getting new interests, taking on new responsibilities, but I can't see any of us waking up one morning a different person. Five years? Hmm, that's roughly the same time we've been at it and we haven't changed in that time."

Marriage?

"Could happen," admitted Don, "and maybe that changes a man, but we'll have to face up to that if and when it arises."

Slade have been earning good money for a couple of years now. Eventually they moved away from their parents and home comforts but they only moved a short distance away.

"Maybe if we had moved to London," explained Dave, "things might have been different. I suppose it *is* possible we might have got big-headed amid the bright lights and hangers-on. But you try getting too big for your bovver boots in Wolverhampton. Nobody gives you the chance!"

THEY'RE HERE NOW AND WE LOVE 'EM . . . BUT WHERE WILL THEY BE TOMORROW??

A MESSAGE FROM
THE SWEET
SPECIALLY FOR YOU

This has been our best year so far and we'd like to thank
every one of POPSWOP'S readers for helping
to make it so. Our love to you all!

WHO'S WHOSE PET??!

There's no doubt about it – animals have a pretty cushy life! Bet you wish YOU could laze around all day, gettin' fat and fed-up! And some of our furry friends really do it in style! Take these ones here f'r instance – they're livin' it up in sheer luxury! You can tell that by just lookin' at them ... but look again ... maybe you can even make out who owns 'em!

PRETTY HEAVY!

Pet No. 1 is called Heavy and he's the private, personal property of Michael Jackson, though Michael doesn't know it yet! He is one of three German Shepherds (extra-special alsatians!) and they all belong to the J5 family. Heavy, however has taken a liking to Michael ... and he makes it pretty obvious! As you'll agree, there are lots of Jacksons to choose from, but, when the boys come home from a tour, guess who Heavy makes a bee-line for?! And when a whole lotta German Sheepdog lands in your lap, it's hard to ignore it!

What's more, he's better than any bodyguard Michael's ever had ... and he's had quite a few! Michael tells us that, although

most of his fans, like you, are really nice to him when they meet, there's always the odd one who gets a bit nasty. And it's at times like these that Mike's glad he's got a pal like Heavy! Heavy, like Mike, enjoys the sunshine and, when Mike has a day or two to himself, you can usually see them sun-bathing together in the J 5's back garden!

SWEET SUSIE!

Pet No. 2 is a beautiful pedigree poodle called Susie and she's the proud owner of Brian Connolly! No, we DIDN'T make a mistake! Truth is that Brian goes all soppy at the mention of her name and she always gets her way with anything she wants! As you kin imagine, she's pretty spoiled. Doggy food's out for a start. She prefers steak for brekky, dinner and tea, 'though she WILL settle for chicken, when times are hard! And, if he really wants to keep her happy, she never says no to the odd bowl of lager on hot days!

Trouble is, she's really very small and, although she's never actually been lost, she's very easily mislaid! Brian remembers one time when the whole group

had dropped by his place, before going onto a gig. They were just about to move out when Brian went to lock Susie in . . . and found she was nowhere to be seen! They turned the place upside down, crawling around on all fours to look under the furniture and calling her name every couple of minutes.

Did they find her? No such luck! Brian was sure she'd nipped out of the front door when the boys first arrived and he was pretty upset. But it was getting late and they'd a job to do, so they got their gear together. Just as Steve Priest was putting his guitar case in the back of the car, it started to jump around. And, when they opened it, they found Susie. She must've gone to sleep inside earlier in the evening. She was pretty near to waking up in Manchester!

CAT BURGLARS!

Recognise the No. 3 twins? They're William and Sammy and they share a flat with Peter Denyer from The Fenn Street Gang! Mind you, three's a crowd and don't they know it. Peter tells us that sometimes they make him feel really unwanted. In fact, if it wasn't that he brings home their food, pours fresh milk into their bowls every day and switches the telly over so that they can see their fave pro-

grammes, he's sure they'd kick him out of the flat!

Still, they're two very pretty Siamese cats and good-lookers always get away with murder! When we saw them, they looked in pretty good nick and Peter told us that was because they got lots of exercise . . . running up'n'down his new velvet curtains!!

Their sleek coats are the result of pounds'n'pounds of very expensive meat, which Pete DOESN'T buy with them in mind! Truth is, they're the trickiest cat burglars in the biz, he says. When he buys fresh meat, they always manage to get to it before he does — no matter *where* he puts it! Most times, it's funny, but once, Pete invited a whole load of people round to dinner. He'd bought in some big juicy steaks which he covered in garlic and herbs and wine and left on top of the fridge till cookin' time. All the guests arrived — very hungry — and the time came for

Pete to make with the cook book. Trouble was, William and Sammy had seen to it that there was nowt left to cook!

BULLS EYE!

That, in case you didn't already know, is the name of David Cassidy's dog — a beautiful red setter, who's our pet No. 4! He's a real man's dog — always wanting to go for walks and quick dips in local streams . . . even in the depths of winter! David isn't always on for that kind of business, so he keeps Bulls Eye on a very long lead, so's David can stay on dry land, while his pet plunges in!

David's also got another dog

called Sheesh. A lady dog this time, 'though you'd never guess it to look at her! Truth is, she's mad about football and plays it even better than David! She really is a bit of a tomboy, which is just as well, since playing with David and Bulls Eye can get to be pretty rough stuff!

CLEO THE CHORUS GIRL!

Meet Cleo! She's a little bit of everything terrier and she leads her owner, Rick Springfield, a dog's life! When we say she's a chorus girl, we're not joking! If she had her way, she'd steal ALL the limelight from our Rick!

Fact is, Rick used to play with a group and they held a few of their rehearsals in Rick's place. Not that Cleo minded — in fact, she was all for it! Often, the group did tapes and they'd spend hours gettin' everything just right. Then, just as the group would be playing the closing

bars of a number, Cleo would join in at the top of her doggy voice, just to help things along!

In the end, they had to ban her from rehearsals. Only trouble was, she had the kind of voice that carried so, even if she joined in from the other end of the house, she could still be heard pretty clearly!

Still, Rick wouldn't change her for the world. He might even let her make a record, someday!!

If you've got a boring old rainy day on your hands, don't sit around moaning that there's *nothing* to do!

THINGS TO DO

1 Make a funny collage for yourself by cutting up old magazines and newspapers. Pick out a lot of contrasting photographs and find funny headlines or captions to go with them. Paste the collection on a large sheet of cardboard, and you've got a decoration for your bedroom wall.

2 Give yourself a facial as good as any salon can! Lock yourself in the bathroom, or your bedroom – fill a basin with boiling water and steam your face over it, making sure all make-up is removed beforehand. Then apply a face-pack to suit your type of skin. Leave it on for about fifteen minutes and remove with cold water. Wait a couple of hours before putting

make-up on again and we guarantee you'll look and feel great!

3 Astound your family with a home-cooked meal! Look through your mum's recipe books for something different to try, get yourself the ingredients and have a bash.

4 Ask your friends over to swop the odds and ends of make-up you don't want. They're probably like you and buy the odd thing on impulse that doesn't suit them in the end – could be their mistakes will be perfect for you, and vice versa!

5 Take up Yoga – if it's good enough for Marty Kristian and countless pop people, it could be good for you! You can get a great paper-back 'Teach Yourself' book by James Hewitt to take you from scratch.

6 Re-arrange your bedroom so that none of the furniture is in the same old position you've liked for years. It's amazing what a difference a turn-about can make to a room!

7 Sort out your wardrobe! Look out all the clothes you haven't worn for ages and have a go at jazzing them up a bit. You can make a fantastic flounced maxi skirt by using an old mini as the first flounce and adding old dress lengths. You can make a plain T-shirt look fashionable by doing a bit of the old lazy-daisy embroidery around the neck, or by cutting the neckline lower and filling in with cotton lace.

8 Drop a line to all those long-lost friends you've been meaning to write to for ages. Or, if you feel you haven't a long-lost friend in the world, send off a couple of letters for Pen-Pals. Get the addresses from the latest POPSWOP!

9 Take a trip to the local swimming baths – actual swimming is great for the figure and if they do Turkish baths or sauna sessions there too, you can give your skin a good deep-cleanse as well!

10 Invite a couple of friends around and dig out those games you've got hidden away. Played with the right people, snakes 'n' ladders, draughts, blow football and Monopoly can pass a few amusing, even hilarious, hours. If you don't believe us, turn to the back page!

We've got twenty ideas to keep you busy and make time fly!

ON A RAINY DAY

11 If it's a real out 'n' out rainy day, store rain-water in the biggest bowl you can find – it's really soft for washing your hair and leaves it naturally shiny and full of life.

12 Paint amazing designs on an old pair of plim-solls or school shoes. Use Lady Esquire or even felt-tipped pens on canvas. Pencil in your design first and then let rip with the creative stuff.

13 Sit yourself in front of the mirror and try out that eye make-up

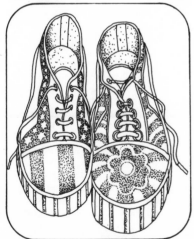

you've always thought a bit daring. Could be it'll suit you and give you a great new look for parties. Experiments you could try are: using pink lipstick as eye-shadow, sticking Marc Bolan sequins with eyelash glue around the eyes, drawing designs in eye-

liner below and around the eye and filling in with shiny shadow.

14 Read that book you've meant to read for ages, but never got around to 'cos reading seemed too much like school work! When the rain's pouring and the money's low, there's nothing quite so nice as curling up in front of the fire with tea 'n' toast and a good novel!

15 Try an afternoon's telly-watching. You'd be surprised how good day-time TV can be – even the programmes for tiny tots are amusing once in a while!

16 Go skating! Try your local roller or ice-rink. If you go with a crowd of friends it's the best sport we know for guaranteeing laughs all round.

17 Go on a crash diet for a day. Experts say that fasting is good for your system, once in a while; it improves both skin and weight! Try living on fruit and water, or milk for the day.

18 Call on that little old lady a few doors away and see if she needs any help around the house, or just stay for a chat. She'll be glad of it and you'll be amazed what interesting tales she'll tell you about her younger days!

19 Catch up on the diary you promised yourself you'd keep. Or look back on the old ones you've got – good for a giggle!

20 Go singing in the rain! If you've got a genuine stormy day on your hands, go for a long blustery walk to get the circulation going a bit. Splash about in puddles, let the rain pelt against your skin, and let your hair get wet 'n' wind-blown. You'll feel really carefree!

Midge n' me!

I'M A GIRL LIKE YOU . . . WITH A FUN LOVIN' FREAK FOR A FRIEND

The trouble with Midge is mostly that she *exists!* I mean, if you haven't met her yet, you probably don't understand what I'm going on about, but it's just not easy, living across the street from the original white tornado.

It wasn't too bad when she slept at the back of her house, but now she's moved her bedroom so it faces mine – "So we can signal to each other," *she* said – *I* haven't had a decent night's sleep! And Mum's been upstairs twice this week, trying to find out why it was raining gravel everywhere!

But I s'ppose I'd better introduce us, before you start thinking it's me who's round the bend.

I'm Jane Marshall, and apart from having Midge as a best friend, I'm quite ordinary and normal really. Midge, on the other hand, is a total lunatic! She's what they call A Big Personality – plus! Which is the nicest way I can think of putting it.

Well, look at this weekend!

My Mum and Dad suddenly decided they were going on their second honeymoon or something and didn't want me with them, so I made the stupid mistake of mentioning it to Midge.

She gaped at me, then did a Morecambe and Wise handclap all round my ears and yelled, "Terrific, Janey! I'll come and stay! We'll have a ball!"

"Now just a minute, Midge," I shook my head to stop it hurting and tried to frown at her, "I was going to my cousin's. It's all been fixed."

"Rubbish!" She gave me this stupid grin and fluttered her false eyelashes. "We'll have a great time. Just the two of us. And you *know* your Mum trusts me."

"Yeah, about as much as she trusts dynamite!"

It was hopeless. I'd've been better off arguing with the street lamp 'cos before I could do anything else, she'd tripped over the gate-post, dashed into the house and was sweet-talking Mum into thinking what a good experience it'd be for us to look after ourselves for the weekend. When I came in, she'd her feet in the jam dish and was muttering things about always wanting to experiment with Cordon Bleu cookery.

I groaned. There's absolutely nothing you can do to stop a natural disaster like Midge when she's started, and anyway Mum had already given her the spare front door key.

So Friday night I came home very slowly – wondering if I could get myself hospitalised, preferably in Outer Mongolia – and there was Midge, covered in a plastic apron, throwing spaghetti at the kitchen walls.

"What on earth . . . ?" I stood there, with my mouth hanging open, as a long white strand wound itself round the electric clock.

"Oh, hi Janey!" she burbled. "Take the weight off your feet. Supper won't be long."

"W–why," I stuttered, "are you doing that?"

She grabbed another handful of the stuff and chucked it round the room. "I read it in a book," she waved the saucepan at me, "but I can't remember if it's done when it sticks to the wall, or if it's got to fall off first."

"Midge!" I yelled, "please, tell me in words of one syllable, *what* are you doing?"

"I *have* told you," she growled, and ducked as a spaghetti strand fell off the ceiling, "I've made us a bolognese."

From the look of the kitchen, she'd made us a bomb site. There were tins and packets and onions everywhere. The electric clock was having a heart attack and looked like somebody'd decorated it for Christmas. The sink was full of washing-up, and when I took the lid off the other pot on the stove, I honestly thought she was cooking Dad's socks!

"Now isn't this nice," she warbled half-an-hour later, through a mouthful of soggy chocolate something. "I think I'll just have my coffee in the sitting-room and watch a bit of telly while you wash up. Okay?"

Have you ever tried to get stuck spaghetti off walls? It's more difficult than climbing Mount Everest, and by the time I'd managed it, tidied up and washed the clock, I was dead!

"I think I'll have a bath," I muttered as I plonked her coffee down beside her. "I feel sort of greasy, and you haven't been any help!" She didn't say a word. Honestly, I've never seen anybody so fascinated in the late-night weather forecast before!

"Okay, Janey," she eventually sighed as I was about to slam the door. "We should both have an early night. I mean, there's all the shopping and everything to do tomorrow. And you know what the supermarket's like."

She was beginning to sound like a suburban housewife with four kids and a starving lawn mower to support, so I just sighed and went up to the bathroom.

I switched on the light, screamed, grabbed a towel – and killed Midge's false eyelashes four times before I realised they weren't spiders! Well, I just hadn't expected her to leave them *in* the bath!

Of course, fairy-feet was up the stairs in a flash, laughing herself sick when she realised what I'd done, so I scowled at her.

"Midge," I coughed, and held out a false finger nail that'd been stuck in the soap dish, "if you don't go away somewhere quietly, I will not be held responsible!"

"Awh, Jane, I'm sorry. I didn't mean it." She was trying to put the finger nail in a very peculiar place.

"You have your bath and I'll bring you a nice hot drink in bed. You're just over-tired."

Over-tired! I was exhausted! I don't usually go in for Spring-cleaning kitchens at eleven o'clock at night.

"Okay," I muttered. "But for Pete's sake don't do anything else!"

I waited until I heard the kitchen door close, then I locked myself in the bathroom and spent about an hour lying in the bath, 'cos it seemed like the safest place.

When I came out, there was a sort of horrible, deathly quiet everywhere — which you don't expect if Midge's in the same house — but I sort of crossed everything and started praying she'd gone to bed.

She had! In *my* bed, wrapped in those awful flanalette pyjamas her Mother makes her wear, cuddling a woolly dog with one ear, and giving little snores every so often.

I just stood and looked at her. It's really quite incredible! I've never seen her asleep before, and she looks absolutely harmless that way! But it was cold in the bedroom, I didn't much fancy the spare room, so after a lot of thought — I sort of pulled at the covers and got in beside her.

"Wassermatter!" She sat bolt upright, clutching her dog and blinking curlers out of her eyes. "Who're you?"

"Awh, come off it, Midge! It's my bed!" I hauled one of the pillows sideways and tried to curl up in about half-an-inch. "Why aren't you in the spare room, anyway?"

"I thought I'd rather be with you. I've never actually stayed in a house all by myself before. And your Mum's taste in wallpaper in that room turns me right off. You don't mind, Jane, do you?" I mean, I *will* go, if you want me to."

I looked at her. She's pathetic! She really is!

"Oh, lie down and go to sleep. You're the one who suggested all this would be good experience."

Two cold bare feet hit me in the small of the back and one of those hairy roller things started to tickle my ear. "Well *you* go and sleep in the spare room," she grunted.

I shoved her feet away and tried to get my ear out of roller-range. "I'm not very keen on the wallpaper, either. Now go to sleep."

She turned over and all the blankets went with her. "Okay. 'Night."

In the end, I s'ppose I must've dozed off, well, there's a limit to how long you can stay awake — even if you *have* got a mouthful of woolly dog — but about four o'clock I suddenly sat up. Midge wasn't in the bed!

I shivered, tried to find the light switch and missed. I've never been on my own in the house either, and I didn't like it any more than she did. I mean, her feet might've been cold, but at least they were *there!*

"Midge," I whispered, and then listened.

Nothing. Just the wind and what sounded like a stair creaking.

"M-Midge?" I tried again, managed to get the light on and peered over the side of the bed.

All I could see were two bare feet, a lot of striped pyjamas and curlers rolled up together, and my quilt which was wrapped up in a ball.

I got out of bed and looked at her.

She was dead to the world, with a great smile on her face, her thumb stuck in her mouth and her woolly dog under her ear.

I asked her in the morning, while she was trying to kill a cornflake, whether she'd fallen out of bed, but she just scowled at me.

"Naturally not," she muttered, and a lot of milk and sugar hit the wall clock, "I just thought you should have a bit more room. After all, it is your bed."

That's the other thing about Midge, sometimes you just don't know whether to believe her or not! But one thing's dead certain, tonight I'm putting that Z-Bed thing Mum keeps under the stairs up in my room. 'Cos if we've *got* to prove how well we can look after ourselves, I reckon at least we can do it in comfort.

And provided the padlock's on the front door — everything should be absolutely fine. Shouldn't it?

THE END

HOW SLADE MADE CHEESE 'N' HAM PIE!

Like we said earlier, popsters are human too and, when they're not hard at work, eating luv'ly grub is one of their fave pastimes!

Slade travel round a lot and at the end of a day, they like a good meal . . . like cheese and ham pie, f'rinstance!

INGREDIENTS (enough for six)
large packet of frozen short-crust pastry
6 ozs. of cold meat, cut up
6 ozs. of grated cheese
1 large onion, chopped up
2 eggs, beaten
salt and pepper
a little milk

You must remember to un-wrap the frozen pastry and let it thaw at room temperature for about an hour before you start cooking. Then you get a loaf tin and grease it with some lard or butter. Roll out two-thirds of the pastry and, when you've rolled it out, so that it's large enough to cover the bottom and the sides of the tin, gently lay it in, allowing a little of the pastry to hang over the edge of the tin. Mix the ham, cheese, onion and egg together and add a bit of salt and pepper. Then pour the mixture into the lined tin. Roll out the remaining pastry until it's about ¼ of an inch thick. Then, damp the edges of the pastry with a little cold water and then lay it over the top of the tin. Press both pieces of pastry together and trim off the excess with a knife. Spread some milk over the top, so that the pastry will brown nicely. Then bake it in a hot oven (Gas No. 6 400°F) for one hour. Let it cool in the tin before serving.

DONNY DIGS CHEESE SANDWICHES!

You know how it is with your fave popster . . . you see him all shimy an' shimmery on the telly and he looks so gorgeous, you're sure he lives in a shole different world. Well, have we got news for you! Popsters ar human too! S'true! They like doing all the things that we do, like laughing, playing, sleeping . . . and eating 'specially!

Donny Osmond, f'rinstance, likes the food things in life – and cheese is one of 'em! He 'specially likes cheesy sand-wiches while he's recording And here's how to make 'em!

INGREDIENTS (enough for one)
2 slices of bread
1 thin slice of cold ham
1 thin slice of Cheddar cheese
butter
French mustard

First of all, you spread the bread with butter on one side. Then you lay the slice of ham on the buttered side of one slice and spread the ham with mus-tard. Then press the buttered side of the second piece of bread down to top of it, to form a sand-wich. Then, you put some butter in a frying pan and, once it has melted, lay the sandwich in the pan and fry quickly on both sides. The bread browns beauti-fully and the cheese inside melts! Scrummy!

LYN'S FOOD'S NON-FATTENING!

Have you ever noticed how all the girls in showbiz are pretty? And it's not just chance, Either! Lyn Paul of the New Seekers told us that, if you want to look good all the time, you've got to work at it! You've got to get rid of all the things that are anti-beauty . . . and that goes for fatty food! Doesn't sound like much fun, we know, but the secret of eating slimming food is to make it look just as interestin' as roast beef an' luv'ly veg! F'rinstance, just see what you kin do with a tomato!

INGREDIENTS (enough for one)
three large tomatoes
1 egg
small piece of cheese

First of all, put the egg in a little water and boil it until it's hard. While it's boiling, take the stalks off of the tomatoes and then stand them upside down (they stand better that way!). Then cut off a slice from what WAS the bottom and is now the TOP of the tomato. With a tea-spoon, scoop out all the insides and place them in a saucer. Then grate the cheese and place it in the saucer as well. When the egg is hard, shell it, cut it up and then put it in the saucer. Mix the whole lot up together, add a little salt and pepper – then spoon the whole lot back into the tomatoes and replace the tops! Put them on a plate and place under a warm grill for a few minutes. They're really delicious and they're not fat-tening!

good grub guide!

MEET MARIE the Unknown Osmond

Poor little Jimmy Osmond sure put his foot in it when he told reporters that sister Marie was about to have her first single released. Suddenly the Osmonds' record company was besieged by non-stop letters and telephone calls asking for the name of the record and when it was coming out.

The truth of the matter was Marie had experimented in the studios and actually recorded a couple of numbers but nobody – maybe with the exception of Marie herself – had thought of putting them out.

So for a little while at least the Osmonds' very pretty sister takes a back seat while her brothers continue their fantastic success story.

Way back in November last year – the night of the group's first-ever concert in Britain at the Rainbow in London – we were lucky enough to be back-stage during the interval. BBC cameras, reporters and assorted guests were flitting about. The Osmonds were being their usual polite and friendly selves, talking to everybody and trying to get ready at the same time.

We were nosing (typical!) round the large room and there in the shadows, sitting all by herself on a drum packing case

was Marie. She was looking a bit glum but was paying careful attention to what was going on, listening to the questions the reporters were asking, listening to big brother Alan tuning his guitar, watching Donny smiling and chatting his way through a photo session as if he didn't know he would be performing in front of three thousand screaming, shrieking, stamping girls in twenty minutes.

We went across and sat down next to her. "Yes," she said, "I *do* feel envious. I wish it were me getting changed to go on stage. I wish it were me the fans were waiting for.

"As you know the family usually travels everywhere together and I spend a lot of time with my brothers. Waiting in the theatre for them to go on is the

> **66 Waiting in the theatre for my brothers to go on is the worst part for me. The excitement is building up and I'm left out of it. 99**

worst part for me. The excitement is building up and I'm left out of it."

Jimmy of course is several years younger than Marie but he gets a solo spot in the act. How come she's kept waiting in the

wings?

Marie smiled and shrugged her shoulders. "I don't know. I guess my mother and father figure a girl needs to be a bit older before she starts working. Also they want to be absolutely sure I want to go into show business and that I have some talent before letting me get out on a stage.

"I'm sure that's what I want to do, I've never really wanted to do anything else. But I don't think I'd be like my brothers . . . I don't know where they get all that energy from. I guess I'd sing quieter songs and just stand there with maybe an orchestra behind me.

"I sure can't see me dancing about like they do."

Being about the same age as Donny, Marie spends a lot of her time chatting with her hearthrob brother. He tells her about his problems and worries. Having seen what fame can mean, doesn't it put her off at all?

"Not now that I've seen how the boys manage," she said.

> **66 I'd rather be famous for being me, than for being my brothers' sister. 99**

"Being part of a big happy family helps a lot."

Marie may not be the big record star she dreams of being, but already she's a big celebrity in America. She has her own magazine columns and even a brand of make-up named after her.

"That's fine," she says with a sad smile, "but I'd rather be famous for being me than for being my brothers' sister."

If Jimmy had his way Marie would be riding high at the top of the pops already. She's going to have to wait a little while longer but we have it on good authority – from Mr. and Mrs. Osmond – that Marie will be releasing records and maybe performing in the not too distant future.

One thing's for sure, she'll know all about backstage nerves. Marie's been getting them on behalf of her brothers for years!

The New Seekers

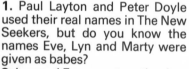

how well do you know 'em?

'Course EVERYBODY knows The New Seekers, don't they? YOU know there are five of 'em in the group and that three of 'em are goodlookin' guys and two of them are nice, friendly girls and one of 'em's Australian, or, summat . . .

C'mon! Try The New Seekers Test, and see how much you REALLY know!

1. Paul Layton and Peter Doyle used their real names in The New Seekers, but do you know the names Eve, Lyn and Marty were given as babes?

2. Lyn and Eve sang together in a group before The New Seekers. What was it called?

3. Recently one of the New Seekers left to pursue a solo career as a singer and entertainer. Can you give his name?

4. Lyn comes from Manchester, something she shares with Peter Noone. What else do they have in common?

5. Either Lyn or Eve only just missed singing on Blue Mink's number one smash hit 'Melting Pot'. Which one turned down the chance in favour of joining The New Seekers?

6. Keith Potger, the group's co-manager gave them their name. Where did Keith get it from?

7. Two of the group's biggest hits have been written by a remarkable American songbird. Who is she and which were the hits?

8. The New Seekers made history when they represented the United Kingdom in the 1972 Eurovision Song Contest. Why?

9. Which New Seeker relaxes with yoga?

10. The group scored a tremendous hit with 'I'd Like To Teach The World To Sing'. Where did the song come from?

11. What was special about the 'Come Softly To Me' single?

12. Which of the girls often works behind a post-office counter at week-ends?

13. Which of the original group made his debut as a television actor in a major long-running series?

14. Eve had to give her toy poodle dog to her mother when she began to travel the world. Do you know the poodle's name? There's a clue in question 10.

15. Only one of the group was born in London. Which one?

16. What lábel do The New Seekers record for? No looking!

17. One of the group was about to join the rock-musical Hair when the offer came to become a New Seeker. Who was it?

18. Lyn is a fully-qualified teacher. But of what?

ANSWERS

1. Evelyn May Beatson, Lynda Susan Belcher and Martin Vanags.

2. The Nocturnes.

3. Peter Doyle.

4. They both acted in the TV series Coronation Street.

5. It was Eve.

6. Keith was a member of the original Seekers, a very successful folk-pop group in the mid-60's.

7. Melanie. She wrote 'Nickel Song' and 'What Have They Done To My Song, Ma.'

8. They were the first *group* to represent the U.K.

9. Marty – and a more relaxed person we've yet to meet!

10. Roger Cook and Roger Greenaway originally wrote the song – with slightly different words – for a Coca Cola TV commercial.

11. Marty was featured on the label as well as on the record.

12. Eve. Her parents run a shop-cum-post office in Perth, Scotland.

13. Dixon Of Dock Green. Paul made his acting debut in the long-running series.

14. Pepsi!

15. Paul.

16. Polydor.

17. Marty. We're glad he changed his mind!

18. Dancing.

36

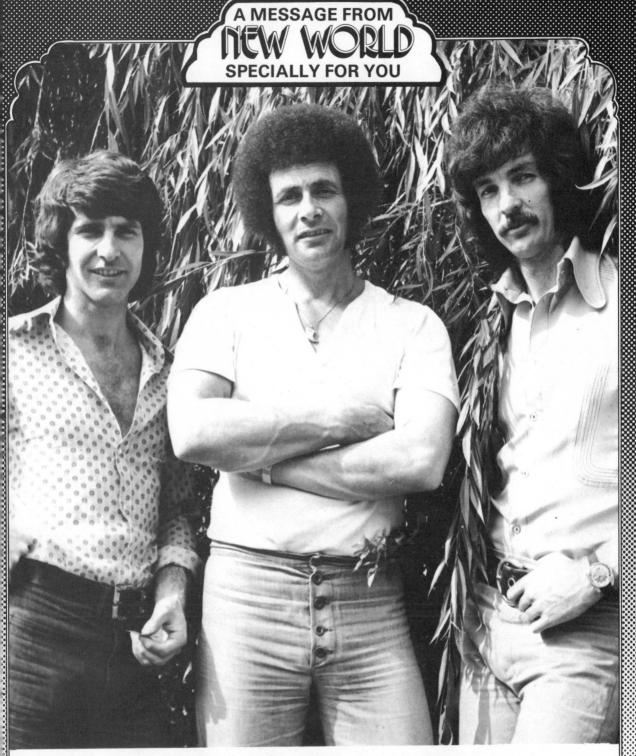

WE LUV YOU, ROD!

You like Rod Stewart? Then you're in good company, 'cos we're crazy about him, too! So much so, that we go around collecting info on him all the time. Lots of it may be useless, but anything about Rod is nice to know!

He was born Roderick David Stewart on January 10th., 1945 . . . and nobody's more pleased about it than us! To begin with, he fancied his chances as a footy player and music never entered his gorgeous head. He played for his school team, along with Kink Ray Davies. He went on to play semi-professional with Brentford . . . but that's when music

began to draw his attention . . .

With a mouth organ and guitar, he trotted off to France and Spain and ended up sleeping on the beaches! Then he came back to England, started getting the breaks and ended up with these luv'ly lads, The Faces! Now he lives in a very grand thirty-room mansion in some quiet corner of Windsor – all seventeen acres of it! His loo is really out of this world, with plaques'n'scrolls'n'gold discs draped over the walls!

But the love of his life is his white Lamborghini – says it makes him feel good just to sit in it! Although he's a bit

of a raver on stage, he's very quiet – shy almost – offstage.

He loves wearing sparkly gear – says he was into it long before anyone else! In fact he loves dressing up off-stage, too! He buys a lot of stuff in Kensington Market, as do lots of popsters we've bumped into, when we've been down there!

And what does he do to relax? Well, he collects old silver, which is a fun pastime, but expensive! A cheaper, if tougher way to have a good time, is playing a game of footy with his old mates, when he goes home for a visit!

There's No Pl

We bet there are times when you – like us – wish you could get a break from the same dull old routine. Not that life's so very bad, in fact it's nothing that a trip round the world, staying in the best hotels and having all your food in restaurants wouldn't solve!! Nice dream, huh? And for some people it actually comes

THE J5'S KITCHEN'S GI-NORMOUS!

The Jackson 5 live in a gorgeous five-bedroomed bungalow in Encino, California, with their mum and dad and sisters La Toya and Janet. Although we've never been lucky enough to see it, we've heard that the place is the last word in luxury!

Their kitchen's bright yellow and really huge! We guess it *has* to be, to store all the food the boys get through! It's full of all the latest gadgets and Ma Jackson makes sure there's always a huge bowl of fruit around, in case the boys get peckish!

The living room is sunken, so you have to go down several steps, before you can sit in the huge circular couch in front of the fireplace. This is the room where all the family meet and the boys keep all their awards on show here, in built-in oak shelves.

At the back of the house, there's a massive swimming pool, where the boys take a dip on warm days. No wonder they're always anxious to get home – it's more gorgeous than any hotel!

The Ryan twins have a flat in London which is the absolute end!! It's all mysterious an' atmosphery, from the minute you step inside the front door! The entrance is covered with deep carpets and has dark red lighting all over. The bedrooms and the bathroom lead off the hall and at the end of it, there's a spiral staircase going down into the lounge.

And the lounge is something out of the glossy mags! The walls are a deep brown and you can't see your feet for carpet, which is a pale, creamy colour. In the middle of the room, there's a kind of 'pit', in which are two couches and a couple of long glass coffee tables. The carpet runs down into the pit and covers the couches and everything! Up above, in one corner of the room, there's a larger-than-life sized statue of a mum, dad and child. And, in another corner of the room there's an indoor pool, with lilies, goldfish and even a little waterfall! The rest of the room is bright with tropical plants, which nearly touch the ceiling. Definitely the kind of place you

e Like Home!

...rue! Everyone we know in the pop biz hardly has time to unpack after one trip, before they're off on another! Some of 'em have been round the world so many times, they've lost count. Some of 'em would give anything for a nice, home-cooked meal of sausage'n'mash. Most of 'em would give the world just to be able to stay at home!!

...never want to leave!

Paul Layton of The New Seekers recently bought himself a fabulous house, but we're not allowed to give out the address! Here's a couple of clues anyway! Maybe you'll be able to work out where he lives, once you've read it. He might even be your next door neighbour!

The house is just off a main road and it's hidden from view by loads of luv'ly apple trees in the front garden. The whole house is built round an open courtyard in the centre of the building. All the doors to the rooms are made of glass and open onto the yard.

The courtyard has trelliswork everywhere, with gorgeous plants climbing over it. In the centre of the yard there's a fountain and there are wickerwork chairs scattered around, in case anyone fancies a bit of sunbathing!

The lounge is very quiet and cool, full of tiled floors and bamboo furniture and, in his bedroom, Paul has a Victorian bedstead, which he searched the whole of England for and which cost him a bomb!

Sounds nice? Well, it looks even better!

When we paid a call on Design, we thought we'd called at a bad moment – things were so chaotic! But they assured us that things were chaotic ALL the time and our arrival didn't make any difference!

The group – made up of four guys and two girls – all live together in a large flat off Cromwell Road in London. But, since they're one of the hardest-working bands around, they're hardly in it! In fact, they say they don't really feel as if they've moved in for good, yet, which is why the place is full of half-painted rooms and bits 'n' pieces of furniture!

When you first get into the flat, you're greeted by a load of musical instruments, which take up most of the hallway! They never have far to travel during rehearsals, 'cos most of the action goes on in their huge living room, one wall of which is almost *all* window! The most eye-catching thing in the room is an enormous grand piano, on which all their harmonies are worked out.

Walk on down a passage and every way you turn, there's a bedroom! There are jeans and dresses lying around everywhere and the odd half-filled suitcase which shows that they've just come from, or are just going somewhere!

There's a bedroom cum office that looks amazingly neat and businesslike. It's painted in orange and white, with a big notice board for clippings of the group and a stack of their recordings. But the kitchen's the nicest place to be. It's full of food! Really it's everywhere, in tins and packets and, providing you can find your way to the kitchen through the maze of rooms, there's no chance of you ever going hungry!

Yep! It's a great place with a lived-in look . . . and six terrific people living in it!

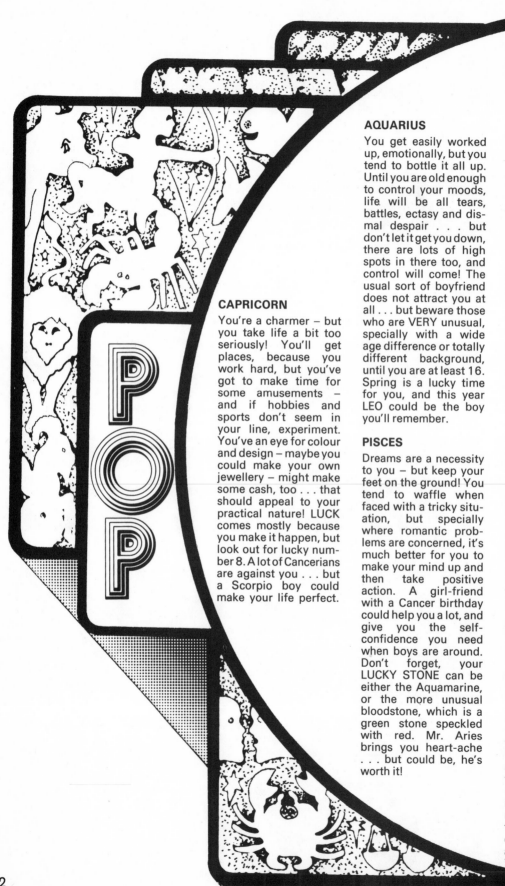

POP

CAPRICORN

You're a charmer – but you take life a bit too seriously! You'll get places, because you work hard, but you've got to make time for some amusements – and if hobbies and sports don't seem in your line, experiment. You've an eye for colour and design – maybe you could make your own jewellery – might make some cash, too . . . that should appeal to your practical nature! LUCK comes mostly because you make it happen, but look out for lucky number 8. A lot of Cancerians are against you . . . but a Scorpio boy could make your life perfect.

AQUARIUS

You get easily worked up, emotionally, but you tend to bottle it all up. Until you are old enough to control your moods, life will be all tears, battles, ectasy and dismal despair . . . but don't let it get you down, there are lots of high spots in there too, and control will come! The usual sort of boyfriend does not attract you at all . . . but beware those who are VERY unusual, specially with a wide age difference or totally different background, until you are at least 16. Spring is a lucky time for you, and this year LEO could be the boy you'll remember.

PISCES

Dreams are a necessity to you – but keep your feet on the ground! You tend to waffle when faced with a tricky situation, but specially where romantic problems are concerned, it's much better for you to make your mind up and then take positive action. A girl-friend with a Cancer birthday could help you a lot, and give you the self-confidence you need when boys are around. Don't forget, your LUCKY STONE can be either the Aquamarine, or the more unusual bloodstone, which is a green stone speckled with red. Mr. Aries brings you heart-ache . . . but could be, he's worth it!

ARIES

You are full of beans an you are just great organising, so ho about channeling som of that gumptio energy and vitality int something really wort your while? You can aim too high! You neve really understand th boys who appeal to yo most, but the main thin is to keep busy and no get too depressed things on the romanti scene sometimes hit th doldrums. You aren usually at your bes when the weather i damp and humid . . sunshine brings out th best in you, and it' worth planning a holi day this year that wi guarantee some sun.

TAURUS

You're very romanti but you've a low opinio of YOURSELF. That's a wrong! You have lots o talent, specially th artistic kind, and yo must jolly yourself u and cultivate your con fidence, to get the mos out of life. Boyfriend are always intrigued b your happy nature bu you have inner depth . . . could confuse a sim ple straightforward typ like Leo, and a romanc with him could drag o more than you'd like Tauran's lucky stone i an emerald.

GEMINI

The original whizz-ban kid! Everyone's going t have trouble keeping u with you – and tha means boyfriends ever more so. Whatever els you may be . . . whic could include fortunat with money, beautiful talented, clever . . . try t be KIND. Some Gemini ans can have a tendenc to be two-faced . . . don' let it be you. You thin it's smart to run tw romances at the sam time, but it bring double heart-ache . . and it might just b YOUR heart that gets it

CANCER

Miss Mouse? Needn't be so! But it'll probably take a certain boyfriend to bring you right out of yourself. You have the kind of looks and figure which takes a little extra special effort to bring out the best – don't go for the obvious when choosing make-up or clothes, but spend more TIME even if you can't spend more MONEY to find the things that really work for you. Don't be a copier! You have a great talent for listening . . . if you can do it without giggling, you'll get boyfriends more exotic-looking girls would envy. Your "type" is Mr. Virgo, so don't be shy!

LEO

The girl with the golden touch could be you. If you'll only work at it, anything you want can be yours. Money – you're too generous to stay rich, but what you give away has a funny way of coming back to you in one way or another. Romance – a slow starter, maybe, but by 18 nobody is more popular than you. Travel – there are some great chances coming your way, so look out for opportunities, specially on the first day of any month.

VIRGO

You're a special sort of person – but don't let it go to your head. You are very particular about things like neatness and hygiene, and you'd rather go dateless than be seen with some spotty, grotty youth . . . but if you are too toffee-nosed about it you'll be sorry, later on. You make too much fuss about your health some-times. Now for the nice things – your special-ness means you COULD get to the top, if you put your effort on to the right track early in life.

LIBRA

If you find life is against you, cheer up because you have such a terrific lot of charm and luck that you really won't be dismal for long – things nearly always seem to bounce your way. Be careful if you have a long spell of fortune, though – don't get conceited, or start treating boyfriends too casually just because the dates are thick on the ground. One unusual thing for you is that your lucky stone is the opal, often thought to be UNlucky for everyone else. One with pinky colours in it would bring you extra-special luck . . . but you must wear it often or the colours fade.

SCORPIO

You love secrets – but don't keep things from your boyfriend! You're inclined to make life difficult for yourself, and if you lose your temper, people will come from miles around to watch the firework display! Try to keep cheerful – the glooms are a definite hazard for you, specially round the 6th day of the month, which is not a lucky date for you. You're versatile and you must remember this – if you get a hard knock, don't just let life flatten you, but try a different approach. You'll find Capricorns can be very helpful, but for romance, look to Sagittarius.

SAGITTARIUS

You're the perfect friend – sympathetic, warm-hearted, cheerful, always good fun to be with. But don't let people take advantage of you! You were born with Jupiter, the lucky planet, influencing your birth, and there is defi-nitely ONE aspect of life which will always be lucky for you. Your job is to find it and the best way is to try every pos-sible opportunity that comes along, every sort of career you can, before finally settling down. Same goes for romance – play the field!

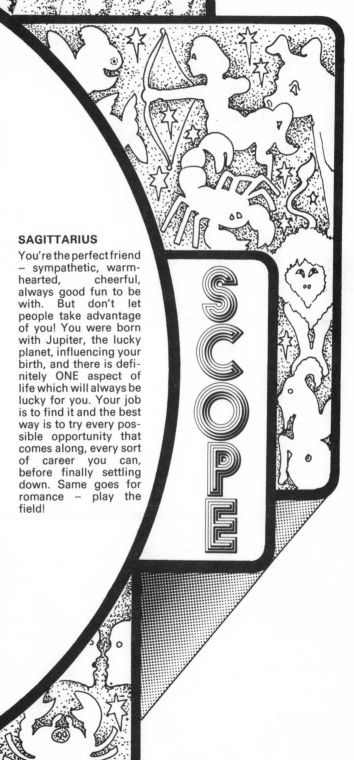

SCOPE

ST[

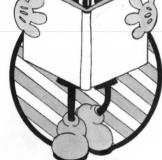

√ a) you're always ready to listen to their problems?
c) there's always something happening where you are?
d) you can always make them laugh?

If you had a spare 60p, what would you spend it on?
√ a) blow it on a little luxury?
d) a ticket for the flicks?
b) some make-up to try out?
ⓒ buying a record?

ⓒ put on your most melting smile and try to soften up the opposition?
b) get someone else to back √ up your argument?
a) sulk, hoping they'll feel bad about it?
d) turn on the tears, knowing they'll do anything for a quiet life?

ROXY CINEMA
60p

What things do you enjoy reading most:
ⓓ romantic stories, where the girl always gets her man?
√ b) anything and everything?
c) dramatic stories, like Wuthering Heights?
a) Walt Disney-type cartoons?

Do your friends like you because:
b) you attract all the best-looking boys?

When there's a row and √ you're not getting your own way, do you:

What colours would you wear together, if you had the choice?
a) cream and brown?
ⓒ red and black?
d) purple with green or pink?
b) blue and yellow?

ARE YOU RSTRUCK?

All of us kinda fancy the idea of becoming famous and, while there are lots of ways of doing it, becoming a famous singer or movie star is definitely the most glamorous! Easier said than done, huh?! But you kin bet that somebody out there, reading this today, is gonna be the big star of tomorrow! . . . and it could just be YOU! Maybe you're the one who has that extra sprinkling of stardust – that magic bit of shimmer which makes you summat special! Why not try our quiz and help POPSWOP to discover you?!

NOW TO FIND OUT IF YOU'VE GOT WHAT IT TAKES TO MAKE A STAR!

Mostly a's

If you're ever going to be a star, you certainly won't be an overnight success! You'll be the type who has a real hard slog, before the fans suddenly discover you! You obviously understand people more than most and, to be a good star, you have to understand human nature. So that's *one* thing to your advantage! Trouble is, though, that you seem to give up easily and you'll have to learn to fight all the way, 'cos there's lots of competition at the top! Your star quality hasn't shown itself just yet, but if you've got it, you'll know all about it soon enough!

Mostly b's

Mmmmm, could be! You're practical and that's important – it takes a girl with a lot of brains to make a little money go a long way and that's what lots of stars have to do, when times are hard! You've got a bit of style, too and that's something else that helps a lot! Maybe you haven't got what it takes to make that extra-special star. But then, fame's a pretty short-lived affair and it's usually the ones who don't make it to the top who have a lot more fun (and money!) half-way up the ladder!

Mostly d's

Well, things are sure lookin' good for you! You're definately pretty, even though you don't quite know it yet and every star-let knows her face is her fortune! You always look just that little bit different when you're in a crowd and, when you're lined up with fifty other girls for a film part, you'll find *that* comes in very handy! Also, you quite enjoy showing-off and that's always good for business. After all, it's no good being a famous star, if you blush at the sight of an audience! Yes, you've definately got all the bits an' pieces that are necessary . . . now all we need to find out is – have you got the talent? It's hard to say just yet, but it could just be that, by the time you're a little older, you'll have found THAT out for yourself!

Mostly c's

We're almost tempted to ask for your autograph! It's bound to be worth a bit of lolly five years from now! What we're trying to say is, you could well be what we've all been looking for – the big star of tomorrow! Not that it comes as any great surprise to you! You've been charming people for years, from your dad, to that new guy on the corner . . . and you're only just beginning! You're bright and pretty and you know it and other people can't help noticing either! Only trouble is, that a girl like you is so busy impressing strangers, she doesn't have time to make real lasting friends. And, as any old star will tell you . . . it's nice to have people you can turn to, when you're not shining just as brightly as you used to!

ON THE JACKSON FIVE
(PLUS RANDY!!)

RANDY JACKSON

Date of birth: October 26th., 1962.
Height: 4' 6".
Weight: 60 lbs.
Colour of eyes: brown.
Colour of hair: brown.
Hobbies: swimming and basketball.
Fave food: enchaladas (Mexican!).
Fave drink: orange juice.
Likes: meeting people.
Dislikes: sitting around 'doing nothing'.
Fave colour: red.
Other info: Randy's very eager to learn – anything and everything! – and all his spare time is spent practising different songs and instruments. Looks like he'll end up one of the most versatile musicians around!

MICHAEL JACKSON

Date of birth: August 29th., 1958.
Height: 5' 0".
Weight: 90 lbs.
Colour of eyes: brown.
Colour of hair: black.
Hobbies: painting, swimming, tennis.
Fave food: Mexican.
Fave drink: Punch.
Likes: travelling, jigsaw puzzles and lizards!
Dislikes: cold weather; people without a sense of humour; waiting in queues.
Fave colour: red.
Other info: Michael's favourite time of the year is Spring (wonder why?). He really enjoys learning new songs and doing concert performances. The two people he'd most like to meet are Fred Astaire and Jerry Lewis.

MARLON JACKSON

Date of birth: March 12th., 1957.
Height: 5' 4".
Weight: 102 lbs.
Colour of eyes: brown.
Colour of hair: brown.
Hobbies: swimming and basketball.
Fave food: steak.
Fave drink: orange juice.
Likes: dancing and drawing – preferably cartoon characters.
Dislikes: being cooped up indoors – he's a great one for fresh air.
Fave colour: brown and blue.
Other info: Marlon's the proud owner of a 'family' of white mice. He's a very sweet guy with a great sense of humour and he loves playing jokes on people! He's very kind-hearted too and a lot of his spare time is spent helping out at local hospital charities.

JERMAINE JACKSON

Date of birth: December 11th., 1954.
Height: 5' 10".
Weight: 165 lbs.
Colour of eyes: brown.
Colour of hair: black.
Hobbies: fishing, songwriting, writing poetry, horseriding, football and basketball.
Fave food: Spanish.
Fave drink: milk.
Likes: laughing, all kinds of sport and going to fun-fairs.
Dislikes: people who are big-headed and who only think of themselves.
Fave colour: red and blue.
Other info: apart from writing poetry, Jermaine is also quite a dab hand at short stories! The ones he likes best are those with sad beginnings and happy endings . . . (ah!).

TITO JACKSON

Date of birth: October 15th., 1953.
Height: 5' 8".
Weight: 130 lbs.
Colour of eyes: brown.
Colour of hair: black.
Hobbies: working on his car and baseball.
Fave food: Tacos (Mexican).
Fave drink: water.
Likes: being able to relax at home with his wife, Delores.
Dislikes: big, formal parties and not being able to meet all his fans.
Fave colour: red and blue.
Other info: Tito thinks that having a private life is very important. He takes his guitar playing very seriously indeed – in fact showbiz itself is definitely his profession – even if he had to give up singing, he'd stay in the business somehow.

JACKIE JACKSON

Date of birth: May 4th., 1951.
Height: 5' 11".
Weight: 165 lbs.
Colour of eyes: brown.
Colour of hair: black.
Hobbies: collecting stereo speakers and basketball.
Fave food: any kind.
Fave drink: Coke.
Likes: the winter months – says he feels more 'alive'; leather and suede jackets and coats.
Dislikes: being known as the 'old man' of the group; not being able to reply personally to *all* his fan mail.
Fave colour: green, brown, beige.
Other info: Jackie's got a real 'business mind' and one day he hopes to go to university to take a business studies course. Meanwhile, 'though he's concentrating on music. He takes piano lessons from a private tutor and he and Jermaine are planning to go to an Arts College to study harmony and musical composition.

CRAZY POP CROSSWORD!

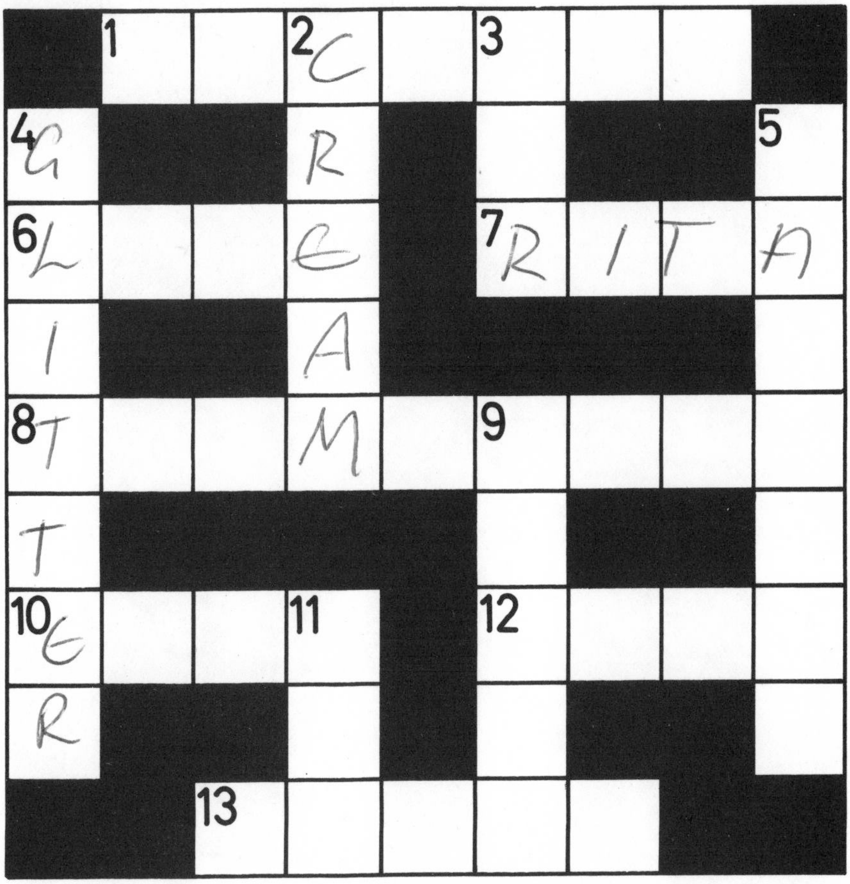

ACROSS.

1. Claim he, perhaps, is one of the Jacksons (7)
6. Gladys Knight sings about the look of it (4)
7. Miss Coolidge? (4)
8. Group formed by Lester and Moe (9)
10. "Doctor My _ _ _ _" (Jackson 5) (4)
12. Greedy Mr. Bowie loses his head (4)
13. "Twelfth of _ _ _ _ _" (Donny) (5)

DOWN.

2. Eric Clapton, Ginger Baker and Jack Bruce (5)
3. "Curved _ _ _" (3)
4. Sparkle like Gary? (7)
5. Mama has three letters for David (7)
9. Go _ _ _ _ _ on a jet plane? (5)
11. Girl with Blackfoot (3)

CROSSWORD SOLUTION

ACROSS:– 1. Michael. 6. Love. 7. Rita. 8. Tremeloes. 10. Eyes. 12. (D)Avid. 13. Never.

DOWN:– 2. Cream. 3. Air. 4. Glitter. 5. Cass-idy. 9. Leave. 11. Sue.

ZOWIE! IT'S BOWIE!

Little or nothing is known about the amazing Mr David Bowie, though he rates as one of the top names in the music world! We at POPSWOP didn't think this was right, so, we quickly got on the blower to the man himself, and gave him the third degree!

Unlike a lot of his fellows in the pop-biz, David didn't change his surname, purely for effect. His current surname came to him, some years back, when he was trying to get known in the pop world, with a line-up called David Jones (that being his real name) and the Lower Third. "We were doing all right, I suppose, when another group – The Monkees – became a big hit, and of course, one of the members was David Jones, so I thought it was time I had a change of name!"

One of David's great love's is art. "When I first left school I joined an advertising agency, as a commercial artist. I quite enjoyed the actual job, but I really found the whole business too cut-throat, so I quit to get some music together."

David's music is very original, he has a style of his own. We wondered if he'd always played this sort of music, or if he had arrived at his own style through various influences. "Well, I guess I've always played the sort of things I do know, though they used to be simpler. But, there was a time when I led a group called David Bowie and The Buzz, when we played progressive blues very loudly!"

Did David ever get tired of the music machine, of the never ending run of tours, we asked him? "It's very exhausting and one often gets depressed. In fact, at one time in my career I did leave music altogether! I formed a mime troupe called Feathers. Then joined a troupe called the Lindsey Kemp Mime Company and was with them for eighteen months. At one of my London concerts, I used the troupe to do theatrical interpretations of my songs!"

Did he get depressed very easily? "Oh god yes, though I try not to let it get me too down. You get so run down when your on the road, too little sleep, irregular meals, that it's not really surprising that eventually you get very low."

If touring got him down so much, we asked him, now that he was a big name, why didn't he cut his tours down a bit? "Don't get me wrong, I don't dislike touring, quite the reverse, it's just very wearing, that's all. I really enjoy going on stage and performing. It was really the performances that got me known. My albums got a lot of critical acclaim, but, like, Hunky Dory, didn't sell as well as a lot of people thought. So, my fame is really pretty recent!"

How did David go about getting together The Spiders From Mars, his backing group? "Well, I got the original members together when I asked guitarist Mick Ronson to join me, he'd been playing in bands for years, and he also played on Hunky Dory. Mick was at one time in a band called Ronno, and two other former members joined me as well, that's drummer Mick Woodmansey, who really knows his instrument, he's been playing drums since he was five, and bass player Trevor Bolder.

Now that he has the music biz all sewn up, had he any other projects he liked to work on? "Well I hope to be in music forever! But I would like to do a few other things as well. I did start an arts lab at one time, I'd like to do that again and acting I'd like to do a lot more of that, but first and foremost for me is my music!" That's fine by us David!

TAKE A GUY LIKE ME (PLEASE!)

Meet Sam, he's almost part of the furniture in the POPSWOP offices – always drinking cups of tea and chatting up the models who drop in! He's a nuisance, but nice with it . . . and he *does* make life more interestin'!

S'all Alfie's fault, innit? The fact that I'm a nervous wreck, I mean.

But maybe I'd better explain, 'cos for all I know – some of you lot may never've heard of me (sigh! sigh!), an' if you haven't, then none of this is gonna make sense!

The name's Sam Watson – place of origin, a grotty little town in the middle of nowhere. An' I've got this mate called Alfie, who's nice 'n' respectable, works in a bank and never does anything he shouldn't. There's nothing actually *wrong* with him – he's just a bit slow, so you have to guide him through the facts of life an' mutter encouraging words in his ear from time to time!

He hasn't much sense of humour, either – comes of spending every day waiting to be held up by masked raiders, I s'ppose. At least, I *thought* that was true, until last night, when I met him for a quick cup of froth an' a biccy in the local caff.

"Sam," he says, and gives this daft great grin, "Have you ever been to Raven Lodge?"

"Eh?" I look at him and wonder what he's got instead of a mind. Raven Lodge is this great old mansion place outside the town that the Council've been talking about pulling down for years. It's surrounded by corrugated iron an' barbed wire, like a holiday camp or something. "As a matter of fact, and to be perfectly honest – no. Why?"

"We-ell," old Alf starts buildin' the sugar lumps into Tower Bridge. "Y'know it's supposed to be haunted? I was walkin' past last night, when there was this funny noise, like a scream, and I saw something at the window. Sorta white 'n' shapeless."

The poor guy's really got himself in a state – I can tell from the way he's demolishing Tower Bridge like he's an R.A.F. bomber. So I lean across the table and pat his hand, all reassuring like.

"Alf," I mutter, "Grow up! There's no such thing as ghosts. They're all tricks of the light an' bits of nylon curtain waving about. It's a well-known scientific fact."

"Yeah, well," he crushes the sugar lumps completely and stares at the gritty bits, "I'm not so sure. That place has got a dead funny feeling about it."

Well, what d'you do? I meantersay, you can't just let poor guys like Alfie suffer for the rest of their days, can you? Frightened to go to bed at night unless the light's on and all that rubbish. So we have a bit more of a discussion an' I suggest we *both* wander along to Raven Lodge, where I can really show him there's nothin' to be scared about.

Only it doesn't work out that way, does it?

We've got it all arranged. I'll nip home, pinch the old man's bicycle light, and meet Alfie outside the lodge gates in about an hour. Then we'll break in, spend a bit of the night there, and if there's any sign of anything that isn't mice, I'll buy Alfie's terrace ticket for Saturday's game.

I have to admit, actually, my stomach's feeling a bit peculiar by the time I reach the lodge, but I put it down to the Chinese meal I had at dinner time and look round for my faithful friend.

Not a flippin' sign. He's only chickened out, hasn't he? He's probably sitting up in his bedroom, with the wardrobe across the door and a poker in his hand, just in case some ghost's comin' to get him!

I wonder for a bit whether it'd be worth-while toggin' myself up in the old lady's sheet and flittin' about in Alf's back yard, but he'd probably flake out on the spot, screaming for mercy and goin' down on his knees or something.

I wait another half-hour. It's pitch-black by now, with that drizzly rain falling over everywhere, and a bit of a wind moaning through the corrugated iron.

"Sam," I say to myself, "there's no point in you hanging about out here. In you go, lad. Over the wall, like in Colditz. Best foot forward. Show 'em you're British!"

So I trot round the side of the barbed wire, find a gap and start to crawl through. The barbed wire's got the seat of my jeans though, hasn't it, an' I don't much fancy spending the night without them, so I struggle as hard as I can, pull free – and find myself in the grounds. There's just one snag – I've gone an' left the bloomin' light on the other side, haven't I?

Anyway, there's a bit of a moon peering through the clouds, an' the house doesn't really look *too* bad. Well, no worse than the buildings you see in all the 'Dracula' films anyway. So I start off up the path.

It's all overgrown, and there's water drippin' everywhere, including down my neck, but I don't see anything that you could call 'supernatural' – unless you count an empty dustbin with a big red cross on it.

I walk about for a bit, wonderin' what's best. If there's a window open, I can get in that way. On the other hand, as Alfie hasn't turned up, I don't really see much point in wasting my time an' catching pneumonia while I'm at it. But I can just hear our Alf if I say I didn't go inside.

"Scared, were you?" he'll cackle. An' if there's one thing I can't stand, it's Alfie's cackle. So I take myself off to the back door an' try the handle.

It only opens, don't it! I s'ppose the Council figured if anybody actually *wanted* to get in, lockin' all the doors wasn't gonna stop them. So I walk through an' find myself in this kitchen place. There's a stone floor an' a fireplace big enough to roast an ox on. But nothing else, except a lot of dust 'n' cobwebs.

By the time I've got upstairs, I'm beginning to wish I'd gone back for the bloomin' torch. I meantersay, old houses *are* a bit weird, in the dark anyway.

But I have a quick shufty in all the rooms an' decide I may as well settle on the landing. That way I'll be able to see in all directions at once – if you follow me.

I've got my back propped against the bannisters, and I'm trying to stop my teeth chattering, it's so bloomin' cold . . . when I hear it!

THUD! CLANK! THUD! Exactly as if somebody was comin' through the hallway draggin' a barrow-load of chains.

I peer through the bannisters, but there's nothing, so I tell myself I imagined it, or maybe the dustmen are on night-work an' somebody's trying to empty the thing with the red cross, when there's this screaming noise.

I can't quite describe it, on account of the fact that, as soon as it starts, I cover my ears an' shut my eyes at the same time. It sounds like a duck in a bad temper, only worse, but it doesn't last long, an' when I open my eyes again – there's nothing. Just a bit of moonlight shining through the broken glass on the staircase window.

"Sam," I growl, "you're gonna go round the twist if you don't catch hold of yourself. Coulda been anything. Coulda *been* a duck. The pond's not far away."

I settle back again, but the house has gone real quiet. Talk about pins dropping – I can hear my heart beat, and I'm not even listening for it!

"Gotta do something," I decide. "Pass the time."

I look at my watch. It's ten off twelve, an' I'd said to Alf we'd stay until midnight, on account of that's when all the ghosts're *s'pposed* to clank their chains, innit?

I get up and have a roam round the landing. There's a room leading off it. Don't know what it was, maybe a library, with this huge chandelier thing in the centre, an' the moonlight's sort of dancing round the glass bits on the top. But it's a bit better than outside, so I settle down and decide I may as well sing or something – just to keep my spirits up.

I'm half-way through my version of "Bridge Over Troubled Water", 'cos it sorta suits my mood, when I realise I can hear breathing.

"Alfie?" I stutter, thinking maybe he's decided to come after all.

There's a sort of swishing, and a blinkin' great draught howls round my ankles, but I can't see anything.

"ALFIE!" I'm on my feet now. "Listen, stop messing about. I'm here!"

Nothing. Just this breathing, like the house has suddenly come alive an' isn't very keen on finding *me* there.

I look at my watch. It's five-past twelve. Then I look out the window. The rain's stopped an' the whole garden's sort of being washed down by moonlight.

For maybe half a second, I thinks I can hear somebody outside calling, "Come home! Come home!" At least, that's what it sounds like. And the swishing in the room's started again.

OK, so maybe it *was* the wind. Or maybe there was a giant mouse runnin' round with a broom in its mouth, keepin' the place tidy. I dunno. An' I don't care if I *never* know!

I get out of there so fast my feet hardly touch the staircase. I'm through the hole in the barbed wire an' half-way down the road before I look back.

It's funny, but just for a second I *thought* I saw something white at an upstairs window, roughly the window I'd been lookin' out of, as a matter of fact.

Not that I'm gonna tell old Alfie any of this, of course, I meantersay, there's no point in worrying him, now is there? He'll just get his ticket for the match on Saturday, an' if he asks any questions – well, I'm feeling generous, aren't I?

But the sooner the Council get their finger out an' pull down Raven Lodge – the happier I'm gonna feel. An' that's for definite!

ELTON'S PHOTO ALBUM
'specially for you!

Everything about Elton John is super! He's super-looking, his singing is super, his clothes are super, his records and concerts are super and .... the photos of him are super! Here's a selection of photos that Elton's 'specially fond of, and we think you'll be 'specially fond of 'em too!!

Elton's mum is very fond of this photo, 'cos it was taken when her 'little boy' was performing in front of the Queen at the London Palladium. Elton certainly went to town with his costume – definitely fit for any Queen!

A quieter Elton is portrayed here. It's pretty rare to find him in a reflective mood, as he's usually larkin' around. But sometimes he can be found just sittin' in some quiet corner reading or – as he was seen to be doing at one recording session – knitting! However, his quiet moods don't last long so you'd have to be pretty quick to catch him in one. In fact, on closer inspection of our pic, do we detect a slight grin appearing??!!

Elton is always knocked-out by his fans' dedication and he loves to meet and talk to them whenever possible! Here we see him doing just that at London Airport. Even though Elton was obviously tired after his long flight from the States, he still made sure that his fans weren't neglected. We bet he made that little girl's dream come true!

Anyone who's ever seen Elton playing, knows just what a fantastic atmosphere he creates. Wow – he certainly knows what the fans want. This photo was taken at one of Elton's concerts and he's really giving it everything he's got . . . which is a lot. It's obvious that music is very important to Elton he enjoys everything he does – it's all fun!

A typical Elton pic is this one. He's wearing one of his favourite outfits. Elton can't stand dowdy clothes, but is quite fond of suits, so this is how he gets the best of both worlds! Mind you, these sorta outfits cost him a pretty penny, but we reckon they're worth it – they make him look a million dollars!

In the background of this pic of Elton you can see masses of his fans! Unlike a lot of popsters, Elton has no fear of bumping into a crowd of his followers, in fact, as you see by his expression, he thrives on it! He's never happier than when he's in a crowd, 'specially a crowd of friends. And that's one of the nicest things about Elton – he considers all his fans his friends!

This last piccy was taken at a recent recording session. From the expression on Elton's face, it's obvious he's concentratin' on giving his best (doesn't he always?) and it must be good, 'cos he's certainly got the full attention of the other musicians! Oh, an' we're not too sure about the fragile but yes, it is Elton John – and he's great!

Hair changes its condition all the time. Partly it's the way you treat it, but it's also very much affected by your health . . . and the weather! So you've got to be prepared to recognise – then deal with – every possible condition from extreme greasiness to extreme dryness. Here's how!

GREASY HAIR handles well immediately after shampooing, but within three days there is an oily sheen and if you don't brush your hair at all, scalp oils will build up, with the result that your hair clings to your head with grease. If you colour-treat or bleach it, at the same time you may notice the tell-tale signs of DRYNESS at the tips (splitting ends, bits breaking off, etc). Other signs that hair is greasier than it should be are combs and brushes that get grubby after two days, pillowslips, collars and headscarves getting dirty much too quickly. After four days, greasy hair gets so lank there's no life in it at all, and it just hangs hopelessly round your face. Trying to push in an extra roller or two won't help, either, the curl just won't set at all. Greasy hair needs tackling urgently, because it's not only pretty unsightly, it's also no help to those of you who suffer from acne.

ACTION: Reban greasy hair treatments, exactly as directed, followed up as the condition improves, with a good lemon liquid shampoo. LIGHT brushing only, to distribute the oil evenly down each hair shaft. CUT OUT eating too many greasy foods. AVOID very hot or very cold water or wearing plastic head coverings. Use special greasy-hair sprays. If you notice split ends, use a greasy-hair anti-splitting shampoo, and choose mild hair colouring and bleaching treatments which have a built-in timing device so they can't over-develop.

DRY HAIR takes several days to settle after you've shampooed it. In dry weather, you've only got to brush it lightly and you'll hear it crackle with static electricity and see it fly up, away from your head! If you ignore these early-warning signals, it will start to get worse quite quickly – straw-like texture, badly split ends, complete unmanageability sets in!

REMEDY? Easy! Your hair is starved – change immediately to enriched shampoos, with any of the following ingredients – olive oil, lanolin, protein, egg. Follow this with an after-shampoo rinse off the creme type, and dry hair at the coolest possible temperature – DON'T bake it under a searing heat. If you do, this lifts the "cuticle scale" on each hair shaft, which gives a roughness to the touch, so hair is difficult to manage. Brush hair as often as possible, for at least five minutes a day. This stimulates the natural oil production and covers each hair with a natural, protective coating of fine oil which gives a glossy look, and makes it easy to handle. DON'T use too-small rollers which, again, damage the outer covering of the hair shaft. Check that your health is o.k. – poor health is the first likely cause of dry hair. Drinking lots of milk, eating cheese, butter, marge and fat-rich fish, eggs and meat

HER
HA

S TO

IR

are essential for shiny, happy hair. Don't be afraid to wash dry hair often. The water won't hurt it, as long as the shampoo is gentle, and the thorough friction and massage your scalp gets in the process helps put matters right. When you set your hair, be extra careful not to damage it with dragging, poor-quality combs — dry hair is delicate hair. Instead, use a brush to clear tangles, then a wide-toothed setting comb.

DULL HAIR that's not greasy, but lank and without any sparkle, is on the danger list because this is often the first stage to hair health problems. Are you wetting it thoroughly before shampooing? If not, the shampoo can't get to grips, so it's not getting a really thorough washing. Are you rinsing for long enough? Dullness can be caused by scum filming the hair, and this is 'specially so where the water is hard. If you're doubtful about your rinsing efficiency, do it for at least three minutes under running water and add some lemon juice (for light hair) or vinegar (for dark hair) to the final rinse. Another possible cause of dullness is using a too-rich shampoo. If you have the idea your hair is permanently dry, it could have changed, but if you still go on using the enriched shampoo, dullness can build up. Too many creme rinses, not correctly used (some need thorough rinsing off — others don't!) can also lead to loss of lustre.

So if all else fails, even if you feel your hair is on the dry side, change to the brightening effect of a lemon shampoo — you can find a cream one, if hair is really delicate. Or use a shampoo-in mild lightener, such as one of the Hiltone Shaders, which brightens without really lifting the colour drastically.

DANDRUFF is not just one disease, but a family! If you see specks of white appearing on your shoulders, no need to panic. But at the same time, you *have* to realise this IS an infection and you must deal with it properly if you hope to clear it. It can vary a lot in seriousness, and because there are several forms of dandruff, the remedy that works for one person may not work for another, so you just have to try different treatments until you find the one that works for you. If you have dandruff once, you are likely to suffer from it again in the future, so when you find, the treatment that works, keep it by you and use it occasionally even when there's none in sight! This is an excellent way to prevent trouble occurring again.

There are many good dandruff shampoos available, but the most efficient are usually the type that require special use, and are not recommended for use week in and week out — only until the trouble clears. Try Lenium first. As your regular anti-dandruff protection, Vosene is first-class, and so is Vaseline Medicated, Clinic. Be fussy about hair hygiene — don't loan combs, brushes, headscarves, and wash everything in contact daily with your hair, as often as you can.

Follow these tips and you'll keep your hair happy . . . and *you* looking gorgeous!

WANTED A WHOLE LOTTA LUCK!

There's no doubt about it . . . a lickle bit of talent can go a long way, if you wanna reach the big time, but there are one or two other things that can help you on your way . . . . . .

Like being in the right place at the right time and meeting the right people when you get there! And the biggest successes sometimes come from the smallest beginnings.

For two people we know, it seemed to all start happening as soon as they changed their names. For a long time, singer Gerry Dorsey tried to make the big time, but never quite got there . . . till he changed his name to Engelbert Humperdinck! On the other hand, there was Paul Raven. Paul became a success in Germany, but it wasn't quite what he wanted. So Paul became Gary Glitter, and since that day, he's never looked back! In fact, he even had a special funeral for Paul Raven, pronouncing him dead, and Gary Glitter alive and well!

Ringo Starr in fact joined the Beatles only a few months before Beatlemania happened. The original drummer of the group was Pete Best and Pete's mum helped to run the group. But, when Brian Epstein took over, Pete was replaced by Ringo, never dreaming what was ahead for him. Ringo used to play, in former days, at places like Butlins, so it was definitely a change for the better!

Also around at the same time, and in the same place Liverpool

was Priscilla White, now known as Cilla Black. Cilla, for extra money, used to work in the cloakroom at the Cavern in Liverpool. Her friends knew she liked to get up and sing on stage when she could, just for a laugh. One night the Beatles were playing and her friends pushed her up. Brian Epstein happened to be around, heard her and signed her up!

Twiggy was just a schoolgirl with a Saturday job sweeping up in a hairdressers. Justin De Villeneuve dropped in to see his hairdresser friend, noticed Twiggy and the thin waif-like quality she had. He immediately saw that in Twiggy there was great potential which eventually would make her the most sought-after model in the world. And he was right.

Sandie Shaw went backstage after seeing Adam Faith, on stage, and while in his dressing room, sang to him. He liked her voice, got his manager to sign

her up, and she became a star. Even more so when they discovered that Sandie preferred to sing with no shoes on. It made her feel more comfortable, and it was an incredible gimmick too, as it turned out. Her feet became her trademark.

Mike Chapman and Nicky Chinn, hit songwriters and managers of The Sweet had a lucky get-together. Mike, an Australian, used to be in a group called Tangerine Peel, but it hadn't worked out, so now he was working as a waiter in the trendy disco Tramps. Nicky, was a customer, and as it was a quiet evening there, they began chatting. They both found they had a lot in common, both wanted to get into songwriting, so they decided to give it a go together. Their list of hits to date would be too long to list, but they include "Little Willy", "Wig Wam Bam", "Blockbuster", "Sister Jane" and "Kara Kara".

One young man who found stardom, short-lived though it may have been was Jimmy Nicol. He was the guy called in to deputise for Ringo on a Beatles tour. Although he was a Beatle for a very short time, a matter of weeks, on the strength of that, he made a disc called "Husky" and it went to No. 1.

It was Twiggy who first gave a helping hand to Mary Hopkin. It was Twiggy who saw her on "Opportunity Knocks", phoned her friend Paul McCartney and told him he must watch her, she was so good. Well, Paul did — recorded her and she became a star. "Opportunity Knocks" of course was the big break needed by Australian group New World, and of course Neil Reid.

Eve Graham and Lyn Paul were old friends from the days they sang together in Manchester with the Nocturnes. So when Lyn heard that they were doing auditions for the New Seekers, Lyn tipped off her friend Eve. Eve was to later return the favour, by telling Lyn that the New Seekers needed another girl, so they were back together again.

Lyn was later to help another old friend, Donna Jones. Donna and Lyn used to sing together when they were very young in the Chrys-Do'lyns. Lyn knew they were looking for a girl singer for Springfield Revival, so told her friend Donna. And Donna, got the job!

Marty Kristian, when he first came to England, had been offered and accepted a role in "Hair". David Joseph, a fellow Australian, heard Marty was in London, and asked him to join the New Seekers, so it was good-bye to Hair!

Peter Doyle came to England with the Virgil Brothers and looked set for success, but they never clicked. Rough days followed, with Peter even sleeping in the underground. Keith Potger of the old Seekers heard that Peter was around, auditioned him, and he became a New Seeker.

So, it just goes to show! Talent obviously counts for a lot, but that little push or break, can make all the difference in the world!

HOW TO YOUR

POPSWOP magazine's pin-up crazy – have you noticed?! Every week, we carry big beautiful piccies like the ones in your annual. Which, the readers tell us, is all very nice. BUT if you've got the sort of dad who says that pin-ups on the new wallpaper are strictly not allowed, what d'you do?
Answer's easy! You find some other way to hang onto your fave popster. Try these for size!

FRAME 'IM!

There's nothing like a frame-up for a fave pic! Firstly, you cut out three rectangles of cardboard, all exactly the same size. The actual size can be anything you like, as long as it's a bit wider and longer than the pic you want to frame.

Cut an oval shape out of the centre of the first piece of cardboard stick your pic carefully onto the second and leave the third plain. Put glue round the edges of the third piece of cardboard and lay the second piece (with the pic) down on top of it. Cover the front of the first piece (the frame) with glue and then sprinkle it with glitter or silver paper or sequins, then leave it to dry. Then glue the back of this piece of cardboard and place it on top of the other two pieces.

To make the stand, cut an oblong of cardboard and fold it into four. The exact measurements for the folds depend on the size of your frame, but make the first section exactly half as wide as the second and third ones (THEY should be the same size) and the fourth section should be three-quarters of the size of either the second or third ones.

Glue the stand together and fasten to the back of your frame!

BEAUTIFUL BADGE

Often in POPSWOP, we print lots of small pics of your fave guys, some in black and white and others in colour. If we print one which you really like, but which would look a bit lost pinned to your wall, try the following!

Take a square of cardboard and stick the pic down onto it. Then, either cut it into a neat circle or heart shape, or cut round the shape of your fella's head, or whatever. Then cover the badge with a piece of adhesive clear film, which can be bought from most stationers' and art shops. Attach a large safety pin, with Sellotape, to the back. Clever, huh?!

HANG ONTO POPSTAR

BOOK BRIGHTENERS!

At the beginning of each new school term, it's the same old story – cover your new school-books, or else! Now brown paper might be the most sensible way of going about it, but you've got to admit, it's hardly the most excitin'! We've come up with a better idea! This term, cover your books with your fave pin-ups! Then you can sit staring at him all dreamy-eyed, when the lessons get to be too much. And think how your covers'll brighten up your evenings, when there's a whole load of homework to be got through! Can't be bad!

ALL LIT UP!

Maybe you're crazy about one particular guy and you spend all your time cutting his luv'ly face out of mags and newspapers?! OK, but what do you do with 'em afterwards? One idea is to get yourself a nice new cream or white lampshade for your bed-side lamp. Make sure your pics have been carefully and neatly cut out and then paste them, one by one on the shade. Next time you turn your lamp on, when you're reading in bed, your fave fella will shine right back at you!

board should be about eighteen inches deep and about three feet long. Cover it with bright material, felt or silver foil and then paste your pics down onto them, one by one. Get dad to put a hook on the wall or on the back of the door (that's the least he kin do!). Then put two tiny nails in the top of the board – one at each corner – and tie the two ends of a piece of string to 'em! Hang it up . . . and hang onto 'im!

STICK 'EM UP!

Another crafty way to keep your cut-outs lookin' good is to get some stiff cardboard, or buy a piece of chipboard from a do-it-yourself shop. Either one is nice'n' light for hanging on the wall. The cardboard or chip-

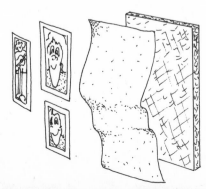

S'true that lots of things in the world are free . . . but it's also true that all the nicest things cost money! Records, make-up natty clothes, tickets to your local disco AND of course, POPSWOP all cost a lotta lolly to

WAYS TO M

1 If you can type quickly it's an idea to invest in a small portable typewriter and take in typing part-time. There are always people with manuscripts, and college notes in need of typing – 'specially if you live near a college or university. The best thing to do is to decide on your rate of charges – perhaps by checking up on the prices of typing services in your area and under-cutting!

2 Take up dress-making for profit. Even if you're not quite in the Mary Quant class, if you can follow a pattern and do alterations, you *could* get a lot of custom. Simplicity do a good book for beginners called 'Let Yourself Sew' – it's helpful.

3 Jam-making is an ancient art, but lots of people still go for home-made flavour.

If you're keen on cooking, it could be worthwhile looking through recipe books for instructions on jam-making. Use fruits when they're in season and follow recipes carefully – they're always easy, but do need patience!

4 You might not reckon yourself as the next best-selling novelist, but you may still be able to make a bit of money by writing. Little poems and funny letters to the readers' pages on newspapers and magazines can bring in a few pounds for a start! If you feel more adventurous, try to write a story or an article about something you know. If you're sending it to a magazine remember it should be typed on one side of the paper only, and you should enclose a stamped addressed envelope for its return.

5 Get yourself a Saturday job. There's no need to think you can only work in the big stores. Hairdressers often need juniors to help with the Saturday rush, and smaller shops and markets need helpers of all kinds.

6 If you can trim your own hair, you may be able to make a few bob cutting hair for your friends and boyfriend's mates. A lot of people don't like going to a hairdresser, so if you pass the word you could get lots of customers.

7 Now that knitted things are so fashionable – 'specially with the hand-knitted look – you could be quids in if you're good with a pair of needles! Once you get used to it, you can probably knit while watching telly every evening.

8 Get a paper-round! You might think this is kids' stuff but, if you're on a keep-fit kick, you could kill two birds with one stone. All that exercise first thing in the morning will keep you in trim, 'specially if you use a bike to get deliveries done quickly.

9 Car-washing is another good way of making money with the minimum of tools. A sponge and a bucket is all you need for most jobs. Ask around your neighbours to see if they're in need of your services – we bet lots of Dads'll be only too pleased to hand the job over to you.

10 You've probably noticed how expensive those big fancy candles are these days. Why not go into business and make your own?!

For one thing, you could do a bomb in a power failure! All you do is melt some cheap wax crayons of the same colour. Pour them into a tin can to set and insert a thin string wick when the wax looks half-set.

11 Go all arty-crafty and make pictures from felt to sell to friends and relatives. All you do is take

get together. Trouble is, there isn't too much of it lying around!

So here we're gonna show you how to make enough money to buy POPSWOPS, till your heart's content!

KE MONEY !

a large piece of chip-board (you can get this cheap from do-it-yourself shops), cover with a large piece of felt and stick one or two contrasting felt squares of varying sizes on in patterns to suit yourself.

12 You don't have to have green fingers to be useful in a garden, so if you like fresh air and flowers you could make money helping to clear up the gardens of big houses around you. Pass the word around that you're willing to clear leaves, tidy paths, pull up weeds and mow the odd lawn for a fee and we bet you'll be kept busy.

13 If you have lots of 'junk' you don't want lying around, don't just throw it into the dustbin. There are shops who will buy old clothes or furniture etc. Perhaps you could see if your neighbours and relatives have things they'd be glad for you to take off their hands, too.

14 when it's coming up to Christmas time, you can make dolls' clothes.

Bet your mum knows lots of people who'd be willing to buy! Buy a few remnants of material from market stalls, get a cheap doll and dress it up.

15 If you fancy your chances as a model, why not ask at local

art schools and technical colleges to see if they need any part-time models for their photography courses – the money's usually good and it's fun!

16 Evening work might seem to you to take up too much precious time, but why not think about taking a job in a coffee bar or a disco? Part-time waitresses and cloakroom girls often get quite a good wage.

17 If you like dogs and exercise ask around to see if anyone in your neighbourhood needs someone to take their dog off their hands for the odd hour. You must remember to keep the dogs on a lead though, and be sure you can handle them!

18 Baby-sitting is one of the sure-fire ways to make money. A small ad in your newsagents' window or local paper should get you lots of work. Needless to say, you must like children and be able to deal with them! The good thing about baby-sitting is that you can usually find time to read if you've got exams coming up!

19 Ask at your local grocery shop to see if they need anyone for bicycle deliveries. It could be they'll be glad of someone to help out with the Saturday rush of orders, or if they don't already deliver, they might be glad of the idea.

20 Become a part-time au pair. If you've got a few day-time hours a week to spare, you could take odd jobs for neighbours or friends of the family. All that vacuuming and scrubbing will be good training for later years and you may even be able to fit it into the odd hour after school!

popfax ON SLADE

DON POWELL

Date of birth: September 10th., 1950.
Height: 5' 11 ".
Weight: 9 sts. 7 lbs.
Colour of eyes: green.
Colour of hair: brown.
Hobbies: none!
Fave food: All-Bran with raisins.
Fave drink: anything free.
Likes: recording, playing live.
Dislikes: not being heard.
Fave colour: blue.
Other info: Don feels that the most important thing about Slade is their stage act. He thinks it's very important for the audience to feel involved, part of the act almost and he really thinks it's great when the audience starts jumping and stomping around! It's pretty hard not to, Don!

JIMMY LEA

Date of birth: June 16th., 1952.
Height: 5' 10".
Weight: 8 sts. 13 lbs.
Colour of eyes: blue.
Colour of hair: brown.
Hobbies: songwriting, reading, films.
Fave food: egg and chips.
Fave drink: vodka and orange.
Likes: films – 'specially late movies on the box!
Dislikes: snow, eating hot spuds.
Fave colour: red.
Other info: Jimmy comes from a very musical family – his grandad used to make the noises for the silent movies and often led the Wolverhampton Orchestra! Two of his great uncles played the violin and his great-grandad played the trombone. His mum tinkles away happily on the piano and also sings! Ever wondered how Jimmy gets that 'heavy' sound from his guitar? Believe it or not, he stuffs the instrument full of cotton wool and screws!! (Honest!).

DAVE HILL

Date of birth: April 4th., 1952.
Height: 5' 6".
Weight: 8 sts. 8 lbs.
Colour of eyes: brown.
Colour of hair: brown.
Hobbies: fishing and films.
Fave food: anything free.
Fave drink: whisky and Coke.
Likes: rings, nice smells.
Dislikes: shaving, washing his feet.
Fave colour: red.
Other info: Dave's just bought a house somewhere in Solihull and it's slap-bang next door to a girls' school! No chance of Dave ever being lonely! At least he'll never have the problem of who's gonna do his washing and ironing – he does it all himself! How many fellas can say that?!!

NODDY HOLDER

Date of birth: June 15th., 1950.
Height: 5' 8".
Weight: 10 sts.
Colour of eyes: blue.
Colour of hair: blond.
Hobbies: films, Agatha Christie.
Fave food: pizza, salad, cheese.
Fave drink: rum and black, Guinness.
Likes: playing live, drinking, and his pet tarantula, 'Sooty'.
Dislikes: cabbage; having his hair cut.
Fave colour: black.
Other info: when Noddy was still a young lad, he had no intentions of making his career in showbiz – in fact he wanted to be a teacher. But while still at school, he won a talent competition and from then on his interest changed from schoolwork to music. Lucky for us!!

A MESSAGE FROM
MARTY
SPECIALLY FOR YOU

All my very best wishes to POPSWOP readers and my thanks
to the crazy POPSWOP gang for all the great things they've
written about myself and The New Seekers. Lots of love from me.

SUPER NOEL'S A SMASH!

He's the king of the punny fun – or should we say the funny pun? His jokes make you cringe, the daft characters he introduces on his show make you want to throw a brick at your tranny. He makes Tony Blackburn sound like Morecambe and Wise yet Noel Edmunds has taken the giant leap from nowhere to top disc-jockey and TV personality in three short years.

How has it all happened? Here's Noel himself to tell you his side of the story!

"Where shall I begin? Ah, the historic day of my birth, that's not a bad place to start! I was born on December 22nd, 1948 at Ilford in Essex. Now you may think that's great for getting a double-helping of pressies what with Christmas just a few days later, but it doesn't always work out that way.

"Anyway, how would you like to wait almost an entire twelve months before getting another parcel? Where were we? Oh yes I went to Brentwood Public School and left in July 1967 proudly clutching my 'O' and 'A' Level Certificates.

"Everybody was expecting me to go to university but something deep down told me to take some time off and have a good think. I was pop mad by then and in between building sports cars all summer I wrote off to pirate radio stations applying for jobs.

"Then it happened – my big break! I got a letter from Radio 355 saying I had the job and when could I start. I hadn't even packed my bags when I heard that the government had closed the station down!"

If I saw my job as just telling listeners the name of a record and who was on it, I'd get out double quick. I mean it doesn't exactly sound an exciting thing to do for twenty years, does it?

So Noel did what came naturally and became a student teacher in Ilford.

"Most of my time was spent taking hoardes of kids around museums and historical buildings. Once we went to the Tower Of London four times in a week. Of course teaching is a very worthwhile and rewarding job but it's important to have some dedica-tion towards it and I'm afraid I didn't."

Noel then joined Radio Luxembourg where he soon established himself as a firm favourite. A year later, he was on the move again, this time to Radio 1, where he worked on trailers, stood in as a holiday relief D.J. and then, in November 1969, he was given his own series.

Noel really dropped into the big league when he took over Kenny Everett's Saturday lunchtime spot and then made Sunday morning his own. Now he's hosting the Monday to Friday Breakfast Show, said to be the prime time on Radio 1.

What does Noel think of his job?

"I've never believed that being a disc-jockey was introducing records and putting them on the turntable. When I get behind a microphone I want to do a show. Built around music of course, but I think it's important to project your own personality and make the two hours or whatever it is as entertaining as possible.

"If I saw my job as just telling the listeners the name of a record and who was on it, I'd get out double quick. I mean it doesn't exactly sound an exciting thing to do for twenty years, does it?

"Of course my humour is corny, it's so bad that you want to shriek, but the audience figures and the letters tell me there are enough people out there who like what I'm doing.

"Music? I've got very wide tastes actually but at home I play mainly softer things . . . Joni Mitchell, Carly Simon. But what I play on the show I enjoy . . . well almost every record!"

Sweet

Cliff Richard

Alice Cooper

Elton John

The Osmonds

David Bowie

Marc Bolan

The Faces

Little Things That Mean A Lot To:

STEVE PRIEST

Steve's a guy who likes to do things on the spur of the moment – one minute he's sittin' quietly watching the ol' box and the next moment he's racing off to a swinging party – never a dull moment! . . . He loves

flying and he thinks airports are great places, says they've got a happy, bustling atmosphere . . . Steve loves old shoes an' he's one special pair that he's had for yonks . . . another fave pastime of Steve's is doodling – he spends hours drawing little cartoon characters! Steve's also very fond of reading newspapers (wait for it!) in the bath!! (It's O.K. so long as he doesn't splash about too much!).

ANDY & DAVID WILLIAMS

They're both sporty lads and love swimming, basketball and football, and when they're not playin' it, then they're watching it on the box . . . Talkin' 'bout telly, it's definitely Mickey Mouse and Donald Duck for them. In fact, if it's a cartoon, then

they'll watch it! They like ice-cream and peanut butter sandwiches (no, not together!) . . . rooms with large French windows . . . riding in lifts! Clothes-wise, it's casual all the way . . . jeans, T-shirts and sneakers . . . they like barbecued food and drink a lot of orange juice and they adore driving in a car with all the windows open!

NODDY HOLDER

Noddy's a real fun guy himself and so it's natural that he likes to see people enjoy themselves . . . He likes

silent movies, 'specially Laurel and Hardy ones . . . He loves bright colours and patterns and he's just mad about salt'n'vinegar crisps! Noddy's favourite form of transport is a train – he likes to sit and stare out the window . . . and he's potty over horror films and adventure comics – the American kind. Naturally, Noddy likes flat caps'n'braces and he had a whole load of 'em sent to him for his birthday . . . oh, and that's another thing he likes – birthdays!

ELTON JOHN

Elton's mad about his latest pair of spectacles . . . He adores soft toys and has got a room full of 'em at his house (most of 'em are life-size too!) . . . Sitting in front of a log fire makes him feel good – he says it beats central heating any day . . . He loves driving his cars, but doesn't often get much time to drive 'just anywhere'. When Elton's hungry, there's nothing he likes better than a quick fry-up of sausage, eggs and bacon (good ol' English grub!). He likes to walk in the rain – as long as it's not too heavy – and he loves to explore old churches – says he finds 'em kinda eerie and mysterious!!

MARC BOLAN

Marc likes everything to do with rock 'n' roll . . . He loves old books and often spends his spare time hunting around book stalls . . . Still on the subject of reading, Marc likes science fiction stories, he says they can be quite revealing!! . . . Marc likes to have people play with his hair – he finds it very relaxing . . . He's fas-

cinated by the Far East, 'cos it's so exotic and mysterious . . . He loves June's (his missus) cooking – 'specially her incredible strawberry gateau! . . . He writes poetry for his own pleasure but likes hearing it read by other people even more . . . He enjoys shopping for clothes, in fact, Marc loves spending money on anything!

ALICE COOPER

Alice likes people – and when he can he chats to his fans for hours! . . . He loves noise and gets quite depressed if things around him stay quiet for too long . . . Alice likes to travel, in fact he hates to stay in one place for too long. Black and red are his favourite

colours and he loves jewellery – he's always buying studs 'n' things to put on his clothes . . . Alice loves the rain and, still on the subject of water, he finds having his hair washed very relaxing! . . . He loves wearing leather and helps to design a lot of his stage clothes . . . Alice loves animals – all kinds (as if we didn't know!!) . . . and he's very fond of his Mum and Dad (ah)!!

eyes right!

There was a time (or so my granny tells me!) when marriages were strictly big business deals. Sweet young things were married off to grumpy old guys or ugly young ones – just 'cos their dads had lotsa loot. Real love and romance was a luxury not many people could afford, so, when a guy asked for your hand in marriage, it was tough deciding whether he wanted you for yourself, or your daddy's fat cheque book! Well, that's not quite true! There was one way, which was never supposed to fail. The idea was that, when this guy looked you in the eye and proposed, you had to stare right back at him and, if he really loved you, it would show in his soft glance! Soppy, I know, but, when things are that desperate, ANYTHING'S worth a try!

That's why we're going to try it out again here. If it's true that the eyes tell all, you should learn a lot from those peepers here. Enough to tell whether the guy behind the gaze is the right one for you, even! Have a look at the eyes first, then see our own analysis – and wait for a surprise.

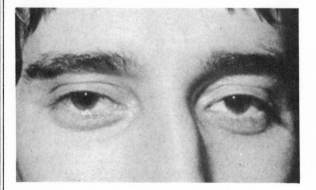

1. It's a bit of a scarey stare, huh?! He's definitely NOT the kind of guy you'd want to take a loan of! He doesn't say much, but what he DOES say, he most certainly means! Like, when he tells you to be there at seven it's best to get there five minutes early! He may seem not to be too interested in all that's going on around him, but really, he's missing nothing. He also knows exactly what he wants and exactly how he's going to get it. He sees a lot in people which isn't obvious to a lot of us, so don't ever try telling fibs to a guy like him – it'll be a waste of your time! If you've chosen this pair of eyes, you like to be kept in line. And if you ever *do* meet up with a pair of eyes like these, you won't be disappointed!

2. As you can probably guess by looking at them, these eyes belong to a real cheeky guy! He's full of mischief and he loves to shock people more'n anything! What's more, he'd like to shock you most of all and, if you met up with him, or someone like him, life would be one long round of practical jokes, incredible outings . . . and a lot of funny friends! He likes people a lot and he wants them to like him in return. He's very aware of what others think of him and he can be easily hurt, so don't be fooled by his couldn't-care-less approach to life!

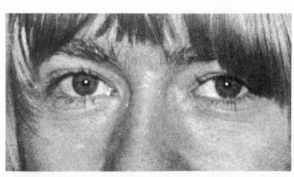

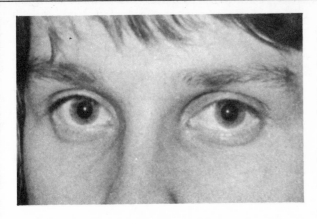

3. Make no mistakes about it, this guy means every word he says . . . and a lot of things he doesn't say. Everything he feels shows in his face so, if you hurt him or upset him in any way, you'll soon know about it. His honest eyes make it impossible for him to tell a good lie, so the chances are if you date someone like him, you'll know exactly where you stand the whole time. When he cares about people, he does everything he can to make them happy. Which is very nice, but it *does* sometimes mean that you try to take advantage of him. Thing is, you'd only have to do it once. If he found out, he'd be off like a flash. So, if you're ever lucky enough to meet him, or his double BE NICE TO HIM!!

4. Recognise those eyes? You should do, 'cos this is a guy who doesn't waste any time enjoying life. He's lucky, 'cos he knows exactly where he's at . . . and he'll expect you to be just the same. He's a leader, 'way ahead of the pack and he wants a girl beside him who can help him set the trend. He's got lots of friends – so many in fact, that none of 'em can get really close. And that's where you'd come in . . . if you were clever! He'd always look to you to level with him. He wouldn't want you to tell him things, just because you think he'd want to hear them. And, because he plays fair, that's exactly how he'd treat you. If a guy like this told you that he loved you, he'd mean it at the time, but don't think it'd last forever. As far as he's concerned, all things must change. It'd be up to you to change with him!

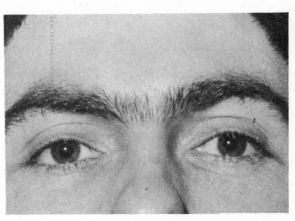

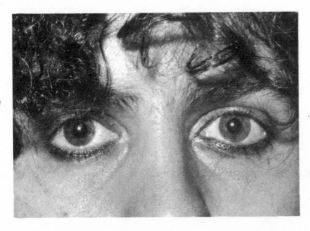

5. You kin tell by the faraway look, that this guy's dreamer – and luv'ly with it! No doubt about it, if someone with eyes like these stared into your face and said he loved you, he'd mean it, all right! The only snag is that, being a dreamer, he won't always see you as you really are. Instead, he'll see you the way he'd like you to be. Very romantic for a while, you'll say, but there's always the chance he'll wake up some fine day and the real flesh and blood you might just come as a bit of a surprise! If you MUST fall for a guy like this, be ready to take everything he says with a pinch of salt. He's got beautiful ideas and dreams he'll let you share, but don't expect them to turn out that way in real life! Still, his type are gorgeous and, if you're a bit of a dreamer too, things could be just too good for words!

There you go, then! You choose the eyes – did the guys come up to your expectations? Wot d'you mean, you don't know who they were?? Surely you've guessed the name of the guy who could be the answer to your prayers?! If not, you'll find them at the foot of this page!

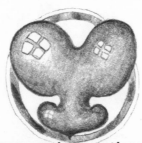

1. Rod Stewart; 2. Brian Connolly; 3. Marty Kristian; 4. Dave Hill; 5. Marc Bolan.

We all know how active the Jackson 5 are on stage – well, off-stage it's the same story. They're an energetic bunch of fellas who really believe in living life to the full and it's certainly no exaggeration to say that there's never a dull moment in the Jackson household!

You've only got to take a look at their house to realise that all the boys are mad keen on sport – in fact it's not so much a house, more like a mini sports' centre! There's a large heated swimming pool, equipped with diving boards and water shute, a basketball half-court, where all the boys play together at least once a day, a badminton court and an archery range – one thing's for sure, the boys will never have to worry about keepin' fit!

Alongside the pool the J5 have built themselves a playroom which is fitted out with pool tables and pinball machines – another favourite J5 hobby! Also in the playhouse is the boys' own personal 'den'. It's here that the boys go when they want to watch T.V., play records, read or just 'be alone' – which, believe us, isn't very often, 'cos the J5 are a family who love to do things together.

Of course, the Jackson 5 have all got their own personal interests. Michael has got a mad passion for art and he often takes off somewhere, just so's he can sit and sketch. He also likes doing jigsaw puzzles – the harder the better! He says it's good to do something that takes a lot of concentration. Naturally music is very important to him and just recently he's got very involved in songwriting. He also loves playing the drums – says it helps get rid of his nervous energy!

Jermaine is definitely a 'fun' character and he's always thinking up new things to do – he can't stand just sitting around. However, when he *does* find himself with a few quiet moments to spare, he uses them to write poetry and short stories. He must be quite a romantic at heart, 'cos he says that the stories he likes best are those with sad beginnings and happy endings!

Jermaine's also an animal lover and he spends quite a bit of time exercising and playing with the J.5's dogs – Heavy, Black Girl and Lobo. Naturally he's fond of all three but will admit that Lobo is his real favourite. Like all the boys, music is important to him and at the moment he's learning to play the piano. (He certainly is a busy lad!).

Marlon is perhaps the quietest one of all. He likes to spend some of his spare time completely alone, just reading or studying. Like Michael, he too is a bit of an artist and he's quite a dab hand at drawing cartoon characters. Marlon's also an expert card player and he's hardly ever been beaten. His brothers are always trying to think up ways to beat him but they usually fail – when

it comes to cards Marlon's too good for any of 'em.

The other Jackson who occasionally likes to spend some time alone is Tito. Tito likes writing music and playing the guitar but he finds that both take a lot of concentration and so he prefers to be alone. Tito's also playing the guitar but he finds that both take a lot of concentration and so he prefers to be alone. Tito's also a bit of a car fanatic and there's nothing he likes better than tinkerin' around with engines and things and, still on the subject of cars, Tito's got himself quite a collection of model cars which he's constructed.

As we said before, all the Jacksons are sport enthusiasts, but perhaps the most dedicated of all is Jackie. He says that the thing he most loves in the world is sport, 'specially basketball, and when he's not actually playing – which isn't very often – then he's watching it on the telly!

O.K. then, that's the five Jacksons covered . . . but we couldn't leave little Randy out could we? As you probably guessed, Randy's a little mischief-maker and he's always getting up to pranks – 'specially in the swimming pool!!?? He loves playing the pinball machines and he says that he's the family champion (mind you, none of his brothers think so!!) and he always joins in when there's a game of basketball on the go. During his quieter moments (very few and far between!) he usually goes of with Michael to sketch. Mind you, now that Randy's started in showbiz with his brothers, more and more of his time is taken up with practising – but Randy doesn't mind one bit, 'cos he's determined to be a success. And if he follows in his brothers' footsteps he shouldn't have too much trouble!!

HOW THE JACKSON 5 GET THEIR KICKS

MEET MARC'S MATES!

Showbiz personalities seem to move in a world of their own, to which only the rich and successful can gain access. One star who can always be found at every glittering gathering is luv'ly Marc Bolan, who looks like becoming the most popular popster around! Not only with *us*, but with the stars as well!

One of Marc's biggest friends is Elton John, and Marc definitely rates top notch on Elton's list too. "Elton and I are great buddies. We often jam together, 'cos we dig each other musically as well as on a personal level. He's played piano for me on quite a few occasions. One of them you'll know about, that was in the movie 'Born To Boogie,' where he was groovin' along with the rest of us. Thinking about that film, reminds me of another mate of mine, Ringo Starr. I can't remember where we first met, but we seemed to hit it off instantly. We had a great laugh, making that film. I wanted a movie to be made of that concert, but I was

having difficulties over it. Ringo stepped in and saved the day and we both enjoyed it so much that we wandered around together for a bit and made it into a full length film! "That bit in the movie where we go, 'Some people like to rock – some people like to roll', well, a lot of people thought that was a put-on, but really it wasn't. We were just having fits about the whole thing – the entire film was like that, it was hysterical! Of course, another good friend is Mickey Finn. I met him 'way back, when the band was called Tyranno-saurus Rex, just after Steve had left me and I was looking for a new bongo player. We were at a party and someone introduced us and told me he played bongos and we were gettin' along so well, that I asked him to come along for a try-out. Which of course, he did! 'Though his singing in those days wasn't much, his voice has improved considerably and he was always an ace drummer. We go around

a lot together, it's a really easy relationship.

Wow, when I think about it, I've got an awful lot of famous pals. There's David Bowie – who I think always dresses incredibly and there's Rod Stewart, and Paul Simon of Simon and Gar-funkel. Not that we're particularly close friends, as he's based in the States and I'm based here, but we hung around together on one of my American tours. In fact, I first met him after one of my shows. He was the last person I expected to see when I got back to the dressing room. I was really knocked out that he'd come to see me, as I've always admired him. He told me he really enjoyed the concert and that he had been dancing in the aisle! Unfor-tunately I haven't seen him for a bit. It's a bit hard keeping track of friends who are always off around the globe, but I *do* try to keep in touch, as *I* think friends are very important, be they famous or otherwise – I didn't really know I had so many real friends until you asked me!"

Noddy's Not Just A Pretty Face!

Noddy's one of the pop biz's wise guys . . . and we mean that in the nicest possible way! He – and the rest of Slade – were quick to notice that success sometimes spoils even the nicest of people and he was determined it wouldn't happen to him! So he's made sure that, no matter how famous an' rich he becomes, he hangs onto his old way of life and his old mates back in Wolverhampton! Nice, huh!

He's a very friendly guy and he's able to talk to you a lot, without actually telling you too much about his private life! But since we're particularly nosey, we managed to get a fair bit of info outa him, 'specially for you!

Did you know, f'r instance, that his real name is Neville Holder – Nev for short? And did you know that the guy he most admired when he was a youngster was . . . wait for it! . . . Al Jolson!! Music for Noddy started with a cheap Spanish guitar, which he taught himself to play, and his first group was called the Memphis Cut-Outs. He could only play with them in the evenings, 'cos he earned his money during the day by selling spare parts for cars!

Being a sensible guy, Noddy knows that rest's important, when you spend your whole life travelling around the world, so he often nips back home and visits his fave pubs, so's he can have a drink and relax with his mates from years ago . . . and his mum's extra-special grub alone is worth the trip North!

Noddy and Slade have been a terrific success everywhere they've gone and all because they're ordinary and matey and not big-headed like some popsters we know. Earlier this year, when they went to Australia on tour, the fans at their concerts went wild! And one Australian girl summed it all up, when she was asked about them afterwards. Her remark? "They're terrific – 'specially Noddy! He's not just a pretty face – he's also a pretty luv'ly fellah!"

GOOD NEWS!!
FOR THINNIES
AND FATTIES!
It's This Way To A Perfect Figure!

PUT A JERK IN IT!

These exercises help BOTH types of dieter! They help firm up the important muscles that control your curves, so that if you're putting on weight, it'll go in all the right places! And if you're taking it off, these exercises will help to control the flab so that you go *in* as you reduce instead of just having ugly folds of skin hanging *down!*

1. GET IT STRAIGHT!

If you stand and move gracefully, your figure improves automatically, without losing or gaining an ounce. Make this one a regular daily routine, first thing in the morning. Stand erect, feet slightly apart, hands on hips. Rotate shoulders forward, up to the ears, back and down, until they feel loose and supple. Do this for one minute.

2. WHO'S BUST?!

Hold a small can of beans (or similar item) in either hand. Sit or stand, body erect from waist. Hold beans with straight arms extended at either side, and gently pull backwards, then relax, to a count of ONE and TWO etc., relaxing on the "and" each time. Begin with a count to 20, and increase daily to a count of sixty. This should take about 1 minute. Aim at bringing arms back behind the body line, if possible.

3. WOTCHER WAIST!

Stand behind a chair, and lightly support yourself by holding the back of it. Swing the upper body as far to the left, then to the right, as you can, keeping feet just a few inches apart for balance. It helps to do this to music. Also, toe-touching exercises and bending to the side as far as you can, make up a good, vigorous routine which you should follow for three minutes daily if you want a trim waist. This is very important when hoping to put ON weight, as you don't want the weight to settle round your middle!

4. HAPPY THIGHS!

Lie on the floor, with your legs straight up in the air, and support your hips with your hands, having your elbows on the floor. Make cycling movements in the air with your legs for two minutes. Psst! The *slower* you can manage it, the more efficiently this one works!

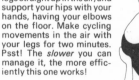

5. BEAUTIFUL BOTTOM!

Sit on the floor with your hands at the back of you, legs apart. Raise left leg and cross it over the right, keeping it straight, trying to touch the ground about two feet away from the other leg – you should feel the hip movement. Repeat with the other leg. Practise for two minutes, daily.

BEEN HAVING A THIN TIME OF IT?

It's nice to be slim, but you can't do without a few nicely-proportioned curves in the right places. If you feel a few extra pounds would improve the looks of your bikini, here's how to go about it . . . but remember it is not so much WHAT you eat as HOW you eat it!

Very skinny people are often the nervous type and, if you bolt your food while thinking of something else, rush about all the time and live on your nerves, you don't have much chance of getting curvy.

GRUB TO GROW BEAUTIFUL ON . . .
Breakfast:

Half a pint of milk. 1 egg. 2 slices of brown bread and butter. If you're rushed, you can still manage this daily if you eat the egg hard-boiled and cook it the night before. When you have time at week-ends, try to have a cooked breakfast with bacon, sausage, etc. If you find half your problem is you can't face breakfast, try having just a warm drink first thing, and then eating a light snack around mid-morning.
Lunch:

Start with an appetiser to settle your tum and work up the juices – NOT soup, which is a filler, but something light and tasty, such as half-a-grapefruit or a little anchovy paste on toast. If you have to eat in a canteen, you could eat a small orange before going in! Avoid rich foods in the middle of the day and concentrate on getting a good protein meal based on meat, fish, cheese or eggs.
Tea:

Try to have a little something before you get over-tired, around four or five o'clock. This is where bread comes in useful – the protein in it gives you more pep to finish the day's work, and if you go without and arrive home exhausted, your body won't be able to cope with a full meal later. Have a small cheese sandwich, or some milk and biscuits, or even a handful of nuts and raisins with your cuppa.
Evening meal:

A good meal, eaten slowly, with plenty of protein, and at least two helpings of vegetables. If you're too full to eat a pudding, have some fruit later in the evening, and end the day with another half-pint of milk.

HOW TO SLIM...AND KEEP SMILIN'!

If you need to lose more than a stone (and 'specially if you need to lose it in less than two months) you need the aid of your doctor. This is most important, because in the process of losing inches quickly you can put your health at risk if you over-do it.

However, if you only want to trim a stone or less, you can do it happily in eight weeks . . . and hardly feel hungry after the first week when, admittedly, you'll notice the difference because of the reduced bulk of your intake!
Breakfast:

Very important! ⅓ pint of milk and a piece of cheese *OR* an egg now will keep you going quite happily until mid-day. If you rush out without this, you are so starving you will be wolfing calorie-rich chocolate biscuits at eleven, and still feel hungry at lunch-time! If you are used to a bigger breakfast, you can have low-calorie starters such as hot lemonade, a grapefruit, or a cup of clear soup. At eleven o'clock, if you feel hunger-pangs in the first week or so, have a cup of tea (low-calorie sweetener, please) and a *WATER* biscuit.
Lunch:

Sandwiches and stodgy canteen food are death, but you can still eat normally with care. If you take your own food, make Danish-style open sandwiches on crispbreads – these travel perfectly if packed in a flat plastic box, each layer separated with waxed paper.

If you eat in a canteen, simply don't take potatoes ('specially chips), pastry and puddings. Base your mid-day meal on a good helping of meat or cheese or fish, but avoid high-calorie proteins like fat pork, oily fish ('specially sprats) and with lots of vegetables and a piece of fruit, you should last the afternoon quite happily.

At four o'clock, it's a good idea to have several cups of tea if you can, and eat a slimmers' biscuit or have a piece of fruit to take you into the evening hours without getting too hungry.
Evening meal:

Finish up what remains of a daily pint of milk, allowing for what you have already had in tea during the day – have this first, to quieten hunger pangs. Some nights, have a bowl of clear soup instead. You are allowed 1 slice of bread or 2 small potatoes at this meal, plus good helpings of meat, fish, cheese, eggs. Two helpings of vegetables, or as much salad as you can eat (not potato salad, obviously!) and a fruity pudding. If you're still hungry, slowly eat a piece of cheese and a stick of celery to finish off with.

ON THE NEW SEEKERS

EVE GRAHAM

Real name: Evelyn May Beatson.
Date of birth: April 19th., 1943.
Height: 5' 4".
Weight: 8 sts. 7 lbs.
Colour of hair: brown.
Colour of eyes: brown.
Hobbies: she's tried lots of different things, but none of 'em last!
Likes: sincere people who always mean everything they say.
Dislikes: getting up early in the morning (that's any time before nine!)
Fave food: home cooking – things like roast beef and apple pies.
Fave drink: almost anything!
Other info: Eve enjoys reading Agatha Christie books and will travel a long way to watch actors like Sean Connery! She plays a lot of Beach Boys music when she's relaxing at home. Eve loves the colour blue and her flat is full of it! She says that one day, when she's very rich she'd like to own a Mercedes – preferably a blue one!!

LYN PAUL

Real name: Lynda Susan Belcher.
Date of birth: February 16th., 1949.
Height: 5' 6½".
Weight: 8 sts. 4 lbs.
Colour of hair: honey blonde.
Colour of eyes: blue.
Hobbies: dancing, collecting silver charms and fluffy toys.
Likes: honesty. She'd much rather hear the truth, than a lie that's told to spare her feelings.
Dislikes: cold rainy days.
Fave food: all sorts of spicy Indian food.
Fave drink: vodka and lime and milk (but not together!)
Other info: Lyn likes wearing yellow and blue outfits. She likes watching

Donald Sutherland and Ali McGraw in action. As you can imagine, she's had a lot of exciting things happen to her but perhaps the most exciting thing of all she tells us, was the first time she went to America. She couldn't believe the view she got from the air, just as the plane was circling before landing.

PAUL LAYTON

Real name: Paul Martin Layton.
Date of birth: August 4th., 1947.
Height: 5' 11".
Weight: 9½ sts.
Colour of hair: brown.
Colour of eyes: hazel.
Hobbies: cars of all shapes 'n' sizes and sport.
Likes: living and everything to do with it.
Dislikes: isn't quite so keen on the thought of dying.
Fave food: he's an expensive boy – he likes oysters and caviare!
Fave drink: plain old water – the colder the better.
Other info: Paul's keen on photography and spends a lot of time and money snapping away. When he was much younger, he was really keen on horse-riding, but he hadn't been in the saddle for years – till he got to Los Angeles, that was! Then he more than made up for lost time! His fave actor is Donald Pleasance. His fave actress is Jane Fonda!

PETER OLIVER

Real name: Larry Peter Oliver.
Date of birth: January 15th., 1952
Height: 5' 10".
Weight: 10 sts. 7 lbs.
Colour of hair: dark brown.

Colour of eyes: brown.
Hobbies: driving and woodwork.
Likes: wearing jeans.
Dislikes: cleaning cars and gardening.
Fave food: steak.
Fave drink: Coca Cola and orange juice.
Other info: Peter loves watching Marlon Brando and Jane Fonda in action on the screen. His ambition is to survive (and why not?!) and he likes wearing the colour green – says it makes him feel lucky!

MARTY KRISTIAN

Real name: Martin Vanegs.
Date of birth: May 27th., 1947.
Height: 5' 10".
Weight: 10 sts.
Colour of hair: dark blond.
Colour of eyes: blue.
Hobbies: he likes hunting around the markets for antiques – 'though he can't always afford to pay for some the luv'ly things he finds!
Likes: playing squash and golf.
Dislikes: nothing. (No doubt about it – he's perfect!!)
Fave food: any vegetarian meal.
Fave drink: fresh orange juice.
Other info: Marty is fascinated by books on the Occult and also on historical books. He was born in Leipzig and his parents emigrated to Australia, when he was only a couple of months old. He studied architecture at Melbourne University and went on to work in an architect's office. Around that time, he performed in the evenings. He first appeared with The New Seekers, when they were doing a stint of shows at the Savoy and the Palladium in London both of which were running at almost the same time!!

A MESSAGE FROM
ANDY & DAVID
ESPECIALLY FOR YOU

We can't believe the great reception we got in London and we
love coming here. Wish we could see all of you but we'll
do our best to see as many of our fans as possible.
Lots of Love

Andy & David

The POPSWOP gang got talking to popsters about the gear they wear on and off-stage and everyone we chatted to told us the same thing . . . they're clothes crazy! Can't say we blame 'em, either! Meantersay, we're always tarting ourselves up with no excuse wotever, so if we were actually goin' to appear on stage or telly at the end of the day, we'd never finish dressin'!

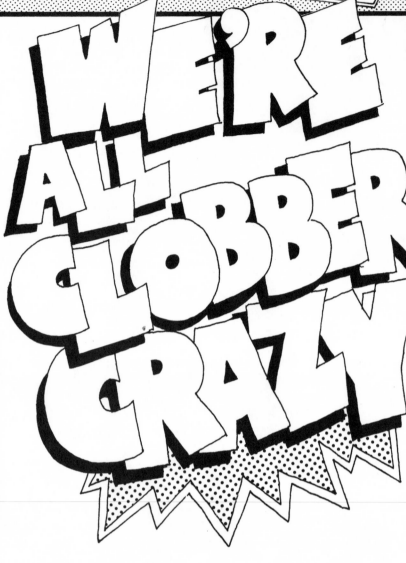

WE'RE ALL CLOBBER CRAZY

T. REX T-SHIRT

For a busy girl like Cilla Black, it's all down to casual clothes. And her favourite outfit for rushing around and rehearsing is jeans and a T-shirt . . . but a *special* T-shirt. The one she likes best of all is black with a tiger on the front, with green stone eyes glittering out. Cilla got it in St. Tropez. Well, actually, she and her husband Bobby were on holiday there with Marc Bolan and his wife. They went into a boutique and both Cilla and Marc fancied this T-shirt. Well, there was only one, so Marc bought it . . . and gave it to Cilla! A very sweet gesture. But, to add a special touch, Cilla likes to wear her full-length mink coat with her jeans and T-shirt!

THE LONG AND THE SHORT OF IT!

A full-time traveller like Eve Graham of The New Seekers has one dress she won't go without! It's a little crimplene crushproof dress she bought in Great Yarmouth a couple of years ago and she's found it's the most reliable dress she has. Lyn Paul however has a favourite outfit that she

uses on stage. At first, you think it's just a pretty long pink dress, but when Lyn expertly rips it off, underneath is revealed a mini white fringed Charleston dress. That always brings the house down!

GETTIN' AHEAD!

Ladies like Carly Simon feel more at home in T-shirts and jeans and floppy hats, and talking of hats, Lynsey de Paul and Paul Layton are two stars who love those hats with the big floppy brims.

COLOURFUL CONNOLLY!

The Sweet of course are a group who love dressing up and are clothes mad. Brian Connolly's favourite stage gear is silver leather trousers and matching waistcoat, but for daytime he still likes things as bright as possible. Lots of yellow, which is his favourite colour.

LOTS OF LUV'LY LEATHER

Marty Kristian, who likes natural food, and naturally good health, also favours natural materials for his clothes. He loves suede and leather, 'specially beigey colours which suit him so well. His favourite is a beige buckskin jacket and trousers, handsown and fastened with thongs. The guy for fringes is Elvis Presley, usually going along his sleeves and across his chest.

AND THERE'S MORE!

Elton John, however won't be seen without his four-inch Cuban-heeled boots, usually silver . . . Donna Jones of Springfield Revival also has a thing about high-heels, but then she *is* tiny. That's why, when fellow Springfield Revivaler Mike Flinn makes himself another pair of leather or suede boots, Donna insists he doesn't stick on any high heels to make her look any shorter, or she'll *never* catch up! . . . Gary Glitter really does like anything that glitters, a part of his image that he's come to love . . . Donny Osmond loves his peak caps, and anything in purple, his favourite colour . . . David Bowie is a creature of change when it comes to

dress, but you can bet anything that whatever he's wearing will be stunning or unusual. It might be a cat-suit, it might be hot pants, but it will be showy and daring whether it reveals his legs or navel! . . . Even Mick Jagger has moved onto the glittered jumpsuit wagon and had his hair cut – and he looks better than ever, and just as young!

These days, people obviously dress to please themselves and couldn't care less about trends. Mind you, when you're a star, you set the trends and people follow you!

D.C's CRAZY 'BOUT ICE CREAM!

MIKE MAKES THE MOST OF BANANAS

NODDY'S NUTS ABOUT OME-LETTES!

Although David Cassidy's a gorgeous-lookin' guy, he's still a youngster at heart! You can tell by the way he loves carnivals and fun-fairs, picnics on the beach . . . and ice cream! Not that there's anything wrong with being an ice-cream lover – *we* suffer from the same complaint! But we've got a nice grown-up way to dress it up – helps you enjoy it even more! It's called Knickerbocker Glory!

INGREDIENTS
3 small blocks of ice-cream (vanilla, chocolate and straw-berry flavours)
1 tin of fruit salad
whipped cream
chopped almonds
raspberry sauce (Tate & Lyle sell it ready-made, in bottles!)
glacè cherries for decoration

Mash each ice-cream flavour seperately with a fork, so that it's soft, but not runny.

Drain the fruit and place two spoonfuls in the bottom of a tall glass. Put a dollop of vanilla ice cream on top of the fruit and follow with a layer of chopped nuts. Then add layers of choco-late ice cream, whipped cream and strawberry ice cream and another layer of fruit. Continue with the layers until the glass is filled. Finish off with whipped cream, sprinkled with a few nuts and a couple of cherries stuck on top. Then cover the lot with raspberry sauce!

Michael Jackson is a pretty sweet guy . . . with a pretty sweet tooth! Though he likes sticky things, he's the sensible kind who keeps an eye on his diet and he gets through an awful lot of fruit every day! We hit on one way of puttin' the fruity things and the sticky things together.

INGREDIENTS (enough for four)
4 bananas (not too ripe)
butter
1 tin of cream
8 tablespoons of syrup

Peel the four bananas and cut the ends off. Lay them in a dish and put two knobs of butter on top of each one. Put them in an oven (350° or Gas Mark 4) and take them out every few minutes, so that you can spoon the melted butter over them. After about fif-teen minutes, they should be cooked and golden. Remove the dish from the oven for five min-utes, to allow the syrup to melt. Serve at once. Delicious!!

When Noddy Holder visited Australia a while back, he dis-covered that it was a big country with wide open spaces . . . and all the fresh air gave 'im an extra-big appetite!

So every night, after a gig, he'd have a slap-up meal . . . and a whole lotta omelettes during the day! Spanish omelettes were his fave – and they'll be yours, too, if you follow this recipe!

INGREDIENTS (for two people)
1 onion, chopped up finely
1 cooked potato, chopped up
2 tomatoes, chopped up
some frozen peas
5 eggs
little milk
salt and pepper
oil for frying

First of all, heat the oil in a frying pan, then fry the onions until golden. Add the potato and fry for a further two minutes, then add the tomatoes and peas. Break the five eggs into a bowl and beat them up with three tablespoons of milk. Pour this mixture over the ingredients already in the pan and raise the heat a little. The eggs should cook in about five minutes. When it's ready, slip it out onto a plate, cut in half . . . and enjoy it!

MICHAEL! DONNY! LOOK OUT!

Alan Osmond and Jackie Jackson may belong to different groups, but they have a lot more in common than you might think!

For a start, both of them are the eldest brothers in sensational world-beating groups. Both of them probably have enough money to live happily on for the rest of their lives. Alan and Jackie both tend to get overlooked by the fans who devote more of their time and tonsils to the younger brothers.

Although you won't find either of them complaining it's a bit unfair to ignore them because they are really the musical strength behind the Osmonds and Jackson 5.

But what really unites Alan and Jackie is the extra responsibility they have of playing not only guitars but playing guardian and sometimes protector to Donny and Jimmy and Michael and Randy.

On tour, it's the eldest brothers who are given the job of looking after the youngsters — making sure they don't get too tired, don't get caught in the middle of a thousand enthusiastic fans and don't get too brought down when things go slightly wrong.

"It's not an easy job," says Alan, "but it's very necessary. After all, nobody looks after family like family.

"Obviously, Donny is the one most in demand for interviews and photo sessions and he finds it very difficult to say, 'Sorry, no more today'. Sometimes, I have to say it for him because he would carry on all night if he thought it was doing the group any good.

"I've known him come home after

BIG BROTHER'S WATCHING YOU!

This is a story for every reader who knows what it's like to have a big bruvver – or sister! – watching her every tiny move!

a busy day, put his head down somewhere and seconds later he's fast asleep. Both Donny and Jimmy have this big thing about proving themselves to the rest of us. I know they wouldn't say a word if they woke up one morning on tour not feeling too good.

"It's my job to watch out for signs that all isn't well and slow things down if I think the pace is getting too hot. Also, being as young as they are, Donny and Jimmy get very disappointed if the smallest thing goes wrong. It's not easy convincing them that it isn't the end of the world if you play a wrong note."

Needless to say Alan is very proud of his two youngest brothers . . . and very pleased they don't give any trouble. "Jimmy can be a bit mischievous,'" he says, "but on the whole the pair of them are great."

As if he needs to tell us that!

Jackie Jackson sometimes feels the need to get into his fast car, put his foot down and vanish for a couple of hours. "I need to get away from my family," said, "because we spend so much time together. I don't resent the success Michael has with his solo records, like a lot of people say. Why should I?"

The Jacksons — like the Osmonds — appeal mainly to younger teenagers and understandably Jackie sometimes gets fed-up, having to watch what he says and does, in case it reflects badly on the rest of the group.

For instance, he'd love to go to the clubs with his cousins Ronnie Rancifer and Johnny Jackson (who play piano and drums in the group's band) but he knows it wouldn't do to be seen out in the wee small hours, no matter how old he is.

But one task Jackie readily accepts is looking after young Michael. In fact he takes that job so seriously he has a secret set of signals worked out with the band.

"If I look at Michael and he looks if he might have difficulty making the end of the song I give one of the signs to the band and they'll cut it short. Sometimes I don't think Michael knows when he's tiring, but I can usually tell and I suggest we have a few days rest."

Young Randy — not yet ten — is now taking part in the group more. That means even more responsibility for Jackie. "As one gets older, another one comes along," he laughed. "But I'm sure we've got to the end of the line now!"

And there was a note of relief in his voice that we're sure Alan Osmond would've understood!

THE THINGS POPSTERS SAY!!

There's no doubt about it – popsters are a fun-lovin' crazy lot! Honestly, when we're interviewing 'em, we fall about laughing at some of the things they say! They always see the funny side of any situation and, in these pics, we've helped 'em along . . . just a little!

POPFAX

ON THE SWEET

BRIAN CONNOLLY

Full name: Brian Francis Connolly.
Date of birth: 5th October, 1949.
Height: 5' 8"
Weight: 9 sts. 8 lbs.
Colour of hair: blond.
Colour of eyes: blue.
Hobbies: swimming, record collecting and target shooting.
Likes: having a drink at the local and girls with lots of personality.
Dislikes: travelling for four or five hours before a gig, as it makes him feel tired and scruffy.
Fave food: steak'n'chips.
Fave drink: lager and lime, 'specially on hot days.
Other info: Brian enjoys listening to Three Dog Night and he likes looking at Sue George! His fave colour is purple and his lucky number is 5. He drives a Capri. Brian's ambition is to be a good all-rounder and he'd like to take up acting some day.

MICK TUCKER

Full name: Michael Thomas Tucker.
Date of birth: 17th July, 1949.
Height: 6'.
Weight: 10 sts. 7 lbs.
Colour of hair: black.
Colour of eyes: blue.
Hobbies: swimming...and he'd like to get together a five-a-side footy team to play against Argent and Deep Purple!
Likes: bright colours.
Dislikes: conceited people and travelling to bookings – sometimes two gigs a night.
Fave food: ham'n'eggs.
Fave drink: an English pint of beer after coming back from a trip abroad.
Other info: Mick enjoys listening to anything from The Beatles to the classics, but his real faves are Tony Bennett, Billy Eckstine, Argent, Yes and (of course!) The Sweet. When asked, he said he didn't have a fave actor but when we pressed the point, he said it was probably Brian Connolly! He has two cars – a Cortina and a Capri and he also has a quarter share in the group's Rover.

STEVE PRIEST

Full name: Stephen Norman Priest.
Date of birth: 23rd February, 1950.
Height: 5' 7".
Weight: 9 sts. 7 lbs.
Colour of hair: red.
Colour of eyes: blue.
Hobbies: telly watching and doing crossword puzzles.
Likes: the colour blue and small girls.
Dislikes: being broke.
Fave food: Mars bars.
Fave drink: cider.
Other info: Steve still lives in Hayes, Middlesex, where he was born. He used to work as a solicitor's clerk and then became an auto-electrician(?!). He likes the music of Led Zeppelin and Jimi Hendrix. Fave actor is David Hemmings and actress is Raquel Welch. Steve drives a Cresta and his lucky number is seven!

ANDY SCOTT

Full name: Andrew David Scott.
Date of birth: 30th June, 1951.
Height: 5' 10".
Weight: 10 sts.
Colour of hair: brown.
Colour of eyes: blue.
Hobbies: reading comedy and Science Fiction books.
Likes: tall slim girls with dark hair.
Dislikes: meeting arrogant people.
Fave food: walnut whips.
Fave drink: freshly-squeezed fruit juice.
Other info: Andy likes watching Gene Hackman and Glenda Jackson on screen. He listens to records by modern jazz artists such as Kenny Burrell and Jimmy Smith. Unlike most people in the biz, he quite likes being alone. He collects guitars and, so far, has two old and battered 'uns as well as five others – three acoustic and four electric. Andy drives a Sunbeam Stiletto and would like to have a go at flying a plane single-handed!

Today David Essex is a star. A bright shining twinkling-eyed star. The most talked and written about stage Jesus ever, following his sensational performance in the hit musical 'Godspell.'

Another brilliant acting display in the film 'That'll Be The Day' has assured him of a great future. But whatever tomorrow holds for David, it has to be better than yesterday . . .

When David was selling apples and pears in an East End street market after school and on Saturdays, he dreamed a dream. He was at Wembley playing soccer alongside his heroes Bobby Moore and Geoff Hurst.

Sadly the dream turned to dust. After a few games for West Ham schoolboys, David decided he was never going to be good enough to make the top grade. The big question was what was he going to do with his life?

His education, as David now tells you, was a disaster.

"It was a real tough school and good teachers stayed a hundred miles away. The local police came at the end of every term to search us for weapons. The thing was, even if you took the trouble to make a good job of the schoolwork it didn't help because your mates would either beat you up or ignore you completely."

"I was in the number one gang, a big leader. I felt I had to go along with it, it was the only way of getting respect."

There was the time David and some pals set fire to the science room!

"It was the old thing about starving with your mates and sticking together through thick and thin. Anyway, we got a six month holiday engagement in Italy and when the others came home I stayed on for a while."

When David returned, he made a couple of solo discs which didn't sell enough to put him into the charts

"Now," he says, "I couldn't tell you why we did it. *Then* it seemed like a good thing to do. Except for the rare occasion when a teacher sparked off something in me, studies never meant a carrot.

David admits that, with his lack of education and dare-devil ways, he could quite easily have ended up with a life of crime. Instead, he discovered music.

"Pop saved me," he says. "I really dug Buddy Holly and Little Richard. I fancied myself as a drummer and kept on at my father to buy me this set of drums in a shop window. I practised and practised and joined a group when I was fourteen.

A couple of years later he was in a blues group, the drummer who had to be the singer as well because in those days blues singers had to have gruff voices and his was the only voice that had broken!

"The band started to get a bit good," David recalls, "and people started coming to see us and waving recording contracts about. The only thing was, it was *me* they were interested in, not the band. I told them all I wasn't interested in leaving the boys.

but got people interested in him. Then he found a manager who figured the pop business was too hit and miss. It depended on finding the right song at the right time so he encouraged David to join a repertory company and learn to act. And David did just that.

He understudied for Tommy Steele as Dick Whittington at the London Palladium. In 1970 he made his film debut in 'Assault' and followed it up with 'All Coppers Are'.

But it was with 'Godspell' that David really took off. The most important critics in the land praised his performance. "It was just what I needed," David told me. "I was in a world really strange to me and it was great knowing that I had been accepted.

That, then is the tale of David's life up until now. Fair takes your breath away dunnit?

On a personal note David is five feet 10½ inches tall and weighs 10 sts. 3 ozs!

He has dark brown hair with dark blue eyes. In what little spare time he gets, he enjoys playing soccer and horse-riding. He's married, has a baby daughter called Verity and lives in . . . Essex!

David's likes include: quiet people, friends, honey, fairy stories, Indian food, motor-bikes, chocolate, flowers, countryside, holidays and the Marx Brothers.

Some of his dislikes are: smoking, discos, sports cars, lazy people, bad manners, too much make-up on girls, beetroot and smelly cafes.

DAVID DOESN'T MISS MUCH!

He's Done A Li'l

Bit Of Everything!

SLADE SCRAPBOOK!

When it comes to polls on who has the most photos taken of themselves, Slade come pretty high on the list. Seems that whatever they do, there's always someone around with a camera just ready to snap them. That doesn't mean that Noddy and the boys get tired of this – on the contrary, they're always pleased to oblige with a pose or two. And from this mountain of pics, the boys have picked out some of the fave photos for you to keep.

Right: Okay, Noddy, we know you're in there! A behind-the-scene shot of Noddy playing tag with a curtain . . . all the bounce and atmosphere that comes across whether on their records or on stage isn't just something the group put on. They've all got great senses of humour, especially Nod, who loves practical jokes of all kind – so beware! All good fun, though, and cheers our lives up, doesn't it?!

Far Left: Loverley Dave Hill's one of the pop scene's most colourful characters, and really nice to boot! Dave's clothes make him pretty noticeable in a crowd, and he designs all his stuff himself. We're not sure who he's pointing to up in the crowd, but we wouldn't minded being the lucky person, so next time Dave, look out for us . . .

Above: Noddy normally has a slightly more active look on his face, which is why he likes this one catching him in a bit of a quiet moment during a show. Noddy's collection of hats is pretty famous now, but he says his favourite article of clothing is baggy pyjamas! Don't reckon it would make much difference to his fans what he wore, as long as he keeps up the good work, and as Noddy's whole life is centred around music and singing, seems like we won't be disappointed.